KU-168-127

LIBRARIES NI
WITHDRAWN FROM STOCK

Costing & Reports

Workbook

NVQ Accounting Units 6 & 7

Janet Brammer

David Cox

Michael Fardon

osborne BOOKS

© Janet Brammer, David Cox, Michael Fardon, 2003. Reprinted 2003, 2004, 2005, 2006.

All rights reserved. No part of this publication may be reproduced, stored in a retrieval system, or transmitted in any form or by any means, electronic, mechanical, photo-copying, recording or otherwise, without the prior consent of the copyright owners, or in accordance with the provisions of the Copyright, Designs and Patents Act 1988, or under the terms of any licence permitting limited copying issued by the Copyright Licensing Agency, 90 Tottenham Court Road, London W1P 9HE.

Published by Osborne Books Limited
Unit 1B Everoak Estate
Bromyard Road
Worcester WR2 5HP
Tel 01905 748071
Email books@osbornebooks.co.uk
Website www.osbornebooks.co.uk

Design by Richard Holt
Cover image from Getty Images

Printed by the Bath Press, Bath

British Library Cataloguing in Publication Data
A catalogue record for this book is available from the British Library

ISBN 1 872962 57 2

Contents

simulations

Unit 6: recording and evaluating costs and revenues

Unit 7: preparing reports and returns

practice examinations

Unit 6: recording and evaluating costs and revenues

Acknowledgements

The authors wish to thank the following for their help with the editing and production of the book: Mike Gilbert, Rosemarie Griffiths, Claire McCarthy, Jon Moore and Pineapple Publishing. Special thanks go to Roger Petheram, Series Editor, for reading, checking and advising on the development of this workbook.

The publisher is indebted to the Association of Accounting Technicians for its generous help and advice to our authors and editors during the preparation of this text, and for permission to reproduce extracts from the Standards of Competence for Accounting and sample assessment material.

Authors

Janet Brammer has over twelve years' experience lecturing on AAT and ACCA accountancy courses at Norwich City College. She is a Certified Accountant and worked in accountancy practice for a number of years. She has also tutored for the Open University and has written a workbook *Management Information Framework* for the ACCA distance learning scheme. Janet is also co-author of *Active Accounting* and *Managing Performance & Resources Tutorial* from Osborne Books.

David Cox has more than twenty years' experience teaching accountancy students over a wide range of levels. Formerly with the Management and Professional Studies Department at Worcester College of Technology, he now lectures on a freelance basis and carries out educational consultancy work in accountancy studies. He is author and joint author of a number of textbooks in the areas of accounting, finance and banking.

Michael Fardon has extensive teaching experience of a wide range of banking, business and accountancy courses at Worcester College of Technology. He now specialises in writing business and financial texts and is General Editor at Osborne Books. He is also an educational consultant and has worked extensively in the areas of vocational business curriculum development.

How to use this book

Costing & Reports Workbook is designed to be used alongside Osborne Books' *Costing & Reports Tutorial* and is ideal for student use in the classroom, at home and on distance learning courses. Both the Tutorial and the Workbook are written for students preparing for assessment on the two units:

- Unit 6: Recording and evaluating costs and revenues
- Unit 7: Preparing reports and returns

Costing & Reports Workbook is divided into three sections: Workbook Activities, Simulations and Practice Examinations. Throughout the text the assessment material has been updated to reflect the changes in the 2003 Standards.

Workbook Activities

Workbook activities are self-contained exercises which are designed to be used to supplement the activities at the end of each chapter in the tutorial text. Many of them are more extended than the exercises in the tutorial and provide useful practice for students preparing for assessments.

Simulations

The practice simulations in this section are written to reflect accurately the changes brought about by the revised 2003 Standards. Osborne Books is grateful to the AAT for permission to use their sample material for the remaining simulations,which have in places been slightly revised for this text, in line with the new Standards.

Practice Examinations

Osborne Books is grateful to the AAT for their kind permission for the reproduction of the AAT Specimen Examination in this section and selected tasks from other Examinations.

answers

The answers to the tasks and exams in the *Workbook* are available in a separate *Tutor Pack*. Contact the Osborne Books Sales Office on 01905 748071 for details of how to obtain the Tutor Pack.

Workbook activities

This section contains activities which are suitable for use with the individual chapters of *Costing & Reports Tutorial* from Osborne Books.

1 AN INTRODUCTION TO COST ACCOUNTING

1.1 (a) Distinguish between cost units and cost centres.

(b) Suggest one cost unit and two cost centres for:
- a firm of accountants
- a parcel delivery company

1.2 Suggest likely cost centres for each of the following:

A theatre in a provincial town, where touring productions are staged. The theatre has a bar and a confectionery counter. Ticket sales are dealt with by the theatre's own box office, and the plays are advertised locally.

A garage, which sells new and used cars of two different makes. Cars are also repaired, serviced and valeted.

1.3 The following cost codes are used by Proton Products Limited:
- factory, 200
- office, 250
- depreciation, 700

State the codes that will be used to charge depreciation to:

(a) the factory cost centre

(b) the office cost centre

1.4 The following are items of expenditure incurred in a company which manufactures clothing. Sort them and enter them into three columns, headed 'Materials costs', 'Labour costs', and 'Expenses'.

(a) Cost of insurance of buildings

(b) Salaries of the office staff

(c) Cost of zip fasteners

(d) Cost of electricity

(e) Wages of storekeepers

(f) Overtime payments for machinists

(g) Cost of a consignment of blue denim

(h) Cost of pre-printed stationery

(i) Cost of television advertising

(j) Cost of cones of thread

(k) Road fund licences for vehicles

(l) Canteen chef's wages

1.5   Which one of the following is normally classed as a fixed cost for a manufacturing business?

(a)   raw materials to make the product

(b)   salaries of maintenance staff

(c)   production workers paid on the basis of work done

(d)   royalties paid to the designer of the product

Answer (a) or (b) or (c) or (d)

1.6   Which one of the following is normally classed as a variable cost for a 'high street' printing shop?

(a)   supervisor's salary

(b)   rent of shop

(c)   electricity used

(d)   cost of paper

Answer (a) or (b) or (c) or (d)

1.7   The following figures relate to the accounts of Manley Manufacturing Limited for the year ended 31 December 2004:

	£
Raw materials used in factory	75,280
Wages of production workers	69,180
Salaries of maintenance staff	30,950
Royalties paid to designer of product	15,110
Depreciation of factory plant and machinery	5,000
Electricity	4,160
Rent and rates	10,290
Salaries of office staff	38,450
Depreciation of office equipment	2,400
Sundry factory expenses	3,020
Sundry office expenses	1,590
Sales revenue	315,840

You are to:

(a)   Prepare a total cost statement for the year which shows:

- prime cost
- production cost
- total cost

Discuss any assumptions that you make and state if you need further information from the company.

(b)   Prepare a profit statement for the year (on the assumption that all the goods manufactured have been sold).

Note: please see the Appendix (page 286) for specimen formats of a total cost statement and a profit statement.

1.8 Bunbury Buildings Limited makes garages and garden sheds which are pre-fabricated as a 'flat pack' in the factory to customer specifications.

You are working in the costing section of Bunbury Buildings and are asked to analyse the following cost items for May 2004 into the appropriate column and to agree the totals:

COST ITEM	TOTAL COST £	PRIME COST £	PRODUCTION OVERHEADS £	ADMIN COSTS £	SELLING AND DISTRIBUTION COSTS £
Wages of employees working on pre-fabrication line	19,205				
Supervisors' salaries	5,603				
Materials for making pre-fabricated panels	10,847				
Cleaning materials for factory machinery	315				
Hire of specialist equipment for one particular job	454				
Sundry factory expenses	872				
Salaries of office staff	6,091				
Repairs to sales staff cars	731				
Depreciation of office equipment	200				
Magazine advertising	1,508				
Sundry office expenses	403				
Hire of display stands used at garden centres	500				
Office stationery	276				
TOTALS	47,005				

2 MATERIALS COSTS

2.1 (a) Suggest:

- two ordering costs

- two stock holding costs

for an organisation that holds a stock of stationery for its own use.

(b) Calculate the Economic Order Quantity (EOQ) from the following information for boxes of 500 C5 envelopes:

- annual usage   200 boxes

- ordering cost   £30.00 per order

- stock holding cost   £1.20 per box per year

Note:

The formula for EOQ is

$$\sqrt{\frac{2 \times \text{annual usage} \times \text{ordering cost}}{\text{stock holding cost}}}$$

2.2 (a) Explain the principles of Just-In-Time (JIT) delivery systems and give one example for a manufacturing business and one example for a service business.

(b) What are the factors that a business or organisation should consider before using JIT for delivery of its purchases from suppliers?

2.3 You are providing accounting help to a friend, Caryl Jones, who has recently set up in business making garden seats and tables. She understands the need to keep records of the different types of timber she has in stock. She has heard of the terms 'first in, first out' and 'last in, first out'; however, she thinks they refer to the physical movement of stock and are not relevant to the pricing of issues to production.

You are to explain by means of a memorandum:

- why FIFO and LIFO are used to price issues of materials

- whether or not FIFO and LIFO relate to the physical movement of stock

2.4 The supplies department of Peoples Bank has the following movements of an item of stock for June 2004:

		units	cost per unit £	total cost £
1 June	Balance	2,000	2.00	4,000
15 June	Receipts	1,800	2.50	4,500
21 June	Issues	3,000		

You are to complete the following table for FIFO and LIFO:

DATE 2004	DESCRIPTION	FIFO £	LIFO £
21 June	Total issue value		
30 June	Total closing stock value		

2.5 Wyezed Limited manufactures a product using two types of materials, Wye and Zed. The accounting policy of the company is to issue material Wye to production using a FIFO basis, and material Zed on a LIFO basis.

The following are the stock movements of materials during the month of August 2004:

Material Wye – FIFO basis

2004		units	cost per unit £
1 Aug	Balance	5,000	5.00
10 Aug	Receipts	2,000	5.25
18 Aug	Receipts	3,000	5.50
23 Aug	Issues	8,000	

Material Zed – LIFO basis

2004		units	cost per unit £
1 Aug	Balance	10,000	4.00
6 Aug	Receipts	5,000	4.20
19 Aug	Receipts	6,000	4.40
24 Aug	Issues	12,000	

(a)   You are to complete the stores ledger records, below, for material Wye and material Zed.

STORES LEDGER RECORD Material Wye									
Date	**Receipts**			**Issues**			**Balance**		
2004	Quantity	Cost	Total Cost	Quantity	Cost	Total Cost	Quantity	Cost	Total Cost
		£	£		£	£		£	£
1 Aug	Balance						5,000	5.00	25,000
10 Aug	2,000	5.25	10,500						
18 Aug	3,000	5.50	16,500						
23 Aug									

STORES LEDGER RECORD Material Zed									
Date	**Receipts**			**Issues**			**Balance**		
2004	Quantity	Cost	Total Cost	Quantity	Cost	Total Cost	Quantity	Cost	Total Cost
		£	£		£	£		£	£
1 Aug	Balance						10,000	4.00	40,000
6 Aug	5,000	4.20	21,000						
19 Aug	6,000	4.40	26,400						
24 Aug									

(b)   At 31 August 2004, the net realisable value of each type of stock is:

- material Wye   £10,000

- material Zed   £44,000

Show the amount at which stocks should be valued on 31 August 2004 in order to comply with standard accounting practice.

2.6   Wyevale Tutorial College is a private college which runs courses for local companies on business and management subjects. The stocks of paper used for photocopying course material are maintained on a FIFO basis at present. The College's accountant has suggested that a change should be made to the LIFO basis.

As an accounts assistant you have been asked to prepare information based on the stock movements of photocopying paper for February 2004 which are as follows:

1 February	Opening stock	100 reams* at £2.10 per ream
5 February	Issues	80 reams
10 February	Purchases	150 reams at £2.20 per ream
15 February	Issues	90 reams
18 February	Purchases	200 reams at £2.25 per ream
24 February	Issues	120 reams
		* a ream is 500 sheets

You are to:

(a)   Complete the stores ledger record shown (see next page) for February, using the FIFO basis.

(b)   Calculate the closing stock value at 29 February 2004 using FIFO and LIFO, and then complete the following table:

Method	Closing stock valuation		
	Quantity (reams)	Cost (£)	Total Cost (£)
FIFO			
LIFO			

	STORES LEDGER RECORD									
	Photocopying paper (reams)									

Date	Receipts			Issues			Balance		
2004	Quantity	Cost £	Total Cost £	Quantity	Cost £	Total Cost £	Quantity	Cost £	Total Cost £
1 Feb	Balance						100	2.10	210

(c)   Write a short memorandum on behalf of the accountant, which explains the difference between the FIFO and LIFO methods of stock valuation. The memorandum will be circulated to members of the College's Finance Committee for discussion and should include your recommendation of the method to be used to ensure that the courses run by the College are not undercosted.

2.7   Go Games Limited sells computer games. At the end of the financial year, the company's stocks include:

300 copies of 'X1X' game that cost £40 each and will sell at only £30, because it is an out-of-date version.

260 copies of a newly-released game, 'X-TRA-G' that cost £56 each and will be sold for £90 each.

100 copies of a current version of 'X-TREME 2' game, which is expected to be up-dated for 'X TREME 3' in the near future. These cost £35 each and normally sell for £55, but because they may soon be out of date, Go Games Limited has reduced the price to £42 each.

You are to:

Calculate the total value of the stock items described above, in order to comply with standard accounting practice.

2.8   A football club shop holds stocks of replica club strip as well as other goods and clothing. The club strip has recently been changed and the old version will have to be sold at greatly reduced prices. At the end of the financial year, the stocks in the shop include:

	Cost	Net realisable value
	£	£
Replica strip (old version)	3,800	2,500
Replica strip (new version)	8,400	11,000
	12,200	13,500

You are to:

Determine the total value of the stock items above, in order to comply with standard accounting practice.

2.9   SummerDaze Limited manufactures plastic garden furniture. Its best seller is the 'Calypso' seat made from white plastic.

The company uses the first in, first out (FIFO) method for valuing issues of materials to production and stocks of materials.

As an accounts assistant at SummerDaze you have been given the following tasks.

Task 1

Complete the following stores ledger record for white plastic for April 2004:

STORES LEDGER RECORD

Product: White plastic

Date	Receipts			Issues			Balance	
	Quantity kgs	Cost per kg £	Total Cost £	Quantity kgs	Cost per kg £	Total Cost £	Quantity kgs	Total Cost £
2004								
Balance at 1 April							20,000	20,000
7 April	10,000	1.10	11,000				30,000	31,000
12 April				25,000				
20 April	20,000	1.20	24,000					
23 April				15,000				

Task 2

All issues of white plastic are for the manufacture of the 'Calypso' seat. The following cost accounting codes are used to record materials costs:

code number	description
2000	stock of white plastic
2100	work-in-progress – Calypso seats
3000	creditors/purchases ledger control

Complete the following table, including the cost accounting codes, to record separately the two purchases and two issues of white plastic in the cost accounting records.

2004	Code	Debit	Credit
7 April			
7 April			
12 April			
12 April			
20 April			
20 April			
23 April			
23 April			

2.10 Barkla Bakery Limited makes fruit cakes which are sold to supermarket chains.

You are an accounts assistant at the bakery; your duties include keeping the records of materials stocks up-to-date.

Task 1

Please refer to the stores ledger record shown on page 20.

- You are to complete the stores ledger record using the information from the materials documentation below and on the next page. You will need to identify and apply the stock valuation method in use. Note that VAT is not entered in the cost accounting records.

- Calculate the balance of stock at the close of the week ending 6 August 2004. Note that it is company policy for returns from production cost centres to stores to be valued at the price of the most recent batch issued from stores.

Task 2

Please refer to the materials requisition and the materials returned documentation below and on the next page.

- You are to complete the column headed 'For cost office use only' on each of these two documents.

MATERIALS REQUISITION

Department: Baking

Document no: MR 112

Date: 5 August 2004

Code no	Description	Quantity	For cost office use only *Value of issue (£)*
DMF	Dried mixed fruit	330 kgs	

Authorised by: *Jan Borthwick*   Received by: *J Trebah*

MATERIALS RETURNED

Department: Baking

Document no: MRN 41

Date: 4 August 2004

Code no	Description	Quantity	For cost office use only Value of return (£)
DMF	Dried mixed fruit	10 kgs	

Authorised by: *Jan Borthwick*

Received by: *J Trebah*

SALES INVOICE
Fruit 'n Nuts Limited
222 Durning Road
Chapeltown TR10 0UP

Invoice to:
Barkla Bakery Limited
Porth Road
Perranville
TR5 8TZ

VAT Registration: 136 2496 82
Date/tax point: 6 August 2004
Invoice number: 4567
Your order number: 821

Description	Total (£)
Dried mixed fruit: 400 kgs at £0.62 per kg	248.00
Goods total	248.00
VAT at 17.5%	43.40
Total due	291.40

Terms: net 30 days

> **BARKLA BAKERY LIMITED**
> Checked against document number *GRN 531*
> Date received *6 August 2004*
> Signed *J. Trebah*

STORES LEDGER RECORD

Product: Dried mixed fruit

Reference: DMF

Date	Receipts				Issues				Balance		
	Document number	Quantity kgs	Cost per kg	Total Cost	Document number	Quantity kgs	Cost per kg	Total Cost	Quantity kgs	Cost per kg	Total Cost
2004			£	£			£	£		£	£
Balance at 1 August									200	0.50	100.00
									300	0.55	165.00
									500		265.00
2 August					109	150	0.50	75.00	50	0.50	25.00
									300	0.55	165.00
									350		190.00
3 August	524	500	0.60	300					50	0.50	25.00
									300	0.55	165.00
									500	0.60	300.00
									850		490.00

3 LABOUR COSTS

3.1 Briefly describe *three* sources that are used to gather information about work done in order to make payment to employees.

3.2 Clock cards are used to calculate:

(a) the wages of employees who work on piecework

(b) the cost of direct materials

(c) the salaries of monthly paid employees

(d) the wages of hourly paid employees

Answer (a) or (b) or (c) or (d)

3.3 HSB Mouldings Limited makes cases for television sets at its modern purpose-built factory. The company uses standard hours produced to measure its labour output.

You are to explain what is meant by a standard labour hour produced.

3.4 An employee makes 160 units of product Exe, 100 units of product Wye, and 250 units of product Zed. The standard labour time allowance per unit is: Exe 5 minutes; Wye 6 minutes; Zed 4 minutes.

What is the number of standard labour hours produced?

(a) 24

(b) 35

(c) 40

(d) 44

Answer (a) or (b) or (c) or (d)

3.5 Renne Limited pays its employees on a time rate, with a rate per hour for a 35-hour week. There are two overtime rates: time-and-a-third for weekdays (rate 1), and time-and-a-half for weekends (rate 2). The details of three employees for last week are as follows:

Employee	Time rate per hour	Total hours worked	Overtime rate 1 (hours)	Overtime rate 2 (hours)
L Constantinou	£ 8.70	40	3	2
H Gunther	£ 9.00	38	–	3
J White	£10.20	42	5	2

You are to calculate how much each employee earned for the week.

3.6 Elend Limited, a manufacturing company, pays its production-line employees on a piecework basis, but with a guaranteed time rate. The details of three employees for last week are as follows:

Employee	Time rate per hour	Hours worked	Production	Piecework rate
J Daniels	£10.00	38	800 units	45p per unit
L Ho	£9.50	35	650 units	55p per unit
T Turner	£9.75	36	500 units	73p per unit

You are to calculate how much each employee earned for the week.

3.7 Brock and Company, a manufacturing business, pays its production-line employees on a time basis. A bonus is paid where production is completed faster than the standard hour output; the bonus is 50 per cent of the standard hours saved and is paid at the actual labour rate per hour. The details of four employees for last week are as follows:

Employee	Time rate per hour	Hours worked	Standard hour output	Actual production
H Hands	£10.50	35	50 units	1,950 units
A Khan	£11.75	37	60 units	2,200 units
T Shah	£11.00	38	50 units	2,000 units
D Smith	£10.80	40	60 units	2,490 units

Note: there were no overtime payments last week.

You are to calculate how much each employee earned for the week.

3.8 Harts Doors and Windows Limited is a manufacturer of double-glazed doors and windows. The company has three production departments – cutting, assembly, and finishing. Data relating to labour for a four-week period is given on the labour cost sheet below.

The company uses a bonus scheme whereby employees receive 50 per cent of the standard hours saved in each department paid at the actual labour rate per hour. This is not included in the actual wages cost (below), which shows actual hours multiplied by the actual wage rate. There have been no overtime payments.

LABOUR COST SHEET for the four weeks ended 26 March 2004			
	CUTTING	**ASSEMBLY**	**FINISHING**
Actual wages cost (£)	6,210	4,214	2,268
Standard hours	556	420	290
Actual hours	540	430	270
Standard hours saved			
Bonus (£)			
Total labour cost (£)			

You are to calculate the total labour cost for each department.

3.9 The production manager at Chucky Chicken Limited, which produces ready-to-cook chicken dishes, has been talking with the accountant (your boss) about the possibility of introducing a system of bonus payments for production-line employees.

The accountant has asked you to draft a memorandum addressed from her to the production manager which sets out the merits of a bonus system for both the company and its employees.

3.10 You are an accounts assistant at Three Oaks Printing Company. One of your tasks is to deal with aspects of the company's payroll. The following queries on this week's payroll have been left for you by the book-keeper:

(a) We paid £400 as overtime to the production-line employees. Should this be treated as a direct or an indirect cost?

(b) There was a machine breakdown in the binding department. As a consequence, production-line employees, who are normally paid on a piecework basis, were paid the time rate for the period of the stoppage, totalling £150. Should this be treated as a direct cost or an indirect cost?

3.11 SummerDaze Limited manufactures plastic garden furniture. Its best seller is the 'Calypso' seat made from white plastic. The payroll for the week ended 18 June 2004 has been completed, with the following amounts to pay:

	£
• net wages to be paid to employees	8,000
• income tax and National Insurance Contributions (NIC) to be paid to the Inland Revenue	1,650
• pension contributions to be paid to the pension fund	850
TOTAL PAYROLL FOR THE WEEK	10,500

The total payroll for the week is analysed as:

	£
• direct labour costs	7,750
• indirect labour costs	1,500
• administration labour costs	1,250
	10,500

As an accounts assistant at SummerDaze you have been given the following tasks:

Task 1

Prepare wages control account for the week ended 18 June 2004:

Dr	**Wages Control Account**	Cr
£		£

Task 2

All of the direct labour costs are for the manufacture of 'Calypso' seats. The following cost accounting codes are in use to record labour costs:

code number	description
2100	work-in-progress: Calypso seats
2200	production overheads
2300	non-production overheads: administration
3100	wages control

Complete the table below to show how the total cost of the payroll is split between the various cost centres of the business.

2004	Code	Debit	Credit
18 June	2100		
18 June	3100		
18 June	2200		
18 June	3100		
18 June	2300		
18 June	3100		

3.12 Perran Limited manufactures surf boards. The following data relates to the production of its 'Porth' brand of board for February 2004:

Total direct labour hours worked	3,000 hours
Normal time hours	2,600 hours
Overtime hours	400 hours
Normal time rate per hour	£10 per hour
Overtime premium per hour	£5 per hour

In the company's cost book-keeping system all direct labour overtime payments are included in direct costs.

The following cost accounting codes are in use to record labour costs:

code number	description
2100	work-in-progress: 'Porth' boards
4400	wages control

You are to:

• calculate the total cost of direct labour for February

• show the cost book-keeping entries, together with account codes, in order to transfer the direct labour costs to work-in-progress

4 EXPENSES

4.1 Terry Hands works for Acme Builders as a member of the direct labour force. However, he has spent the last two weeks re-decorating the company's offices.

How should his wages for this period be dealt with in the accounts? Why is this?

4.2 Classify the following costs (tick the appropriate column):

	capital expenditure	revenue expenditure
(a) building an extension to the administration office		
(b) cleaning materials for factory machinery		
(c) repair of office photocopier		
(d) directors' salaries		
(e) carriage inwards on new machinery		
(f) carriage inwards on raw materials		
(g) installation of computer system		
(h) insurance of computer system		
(i) installation of special wiring for computer system		

4.3 Classify the following costs (tick the appropriate column):

	DIRECT EXPENSES	INDIRECT EXPENSES	
		production overheads	non-production overheads
(a) royalties paid to designer of product			
(b) straight-line depreciation of factory machinery			
(c) office electricity			
(d) insurance of factory buildings			
(e) advertising			
(f) rent on factory			
(g) units of output depreciation of factory machinery			
(h) factory manager's car expenses			
(i) sales department administration			

4.4 Jarvis Trading Limited depreciates its vehicles at 25 per cent per year, using the reducing balance method.

A car for the sales department was bought on 1 January 2004 at a cost of £16,000.

You are to calculate the depreciation amounts for 2004, 2005 and 2006, and to show the residual value at 31 December 2006. (Note: the company's financial year end is 31 December.)

4.5   Cradley Castings Limited has recently bought a new casting machine for which the details are as follows:

CASTING MACHINE

Cost price on 1 January 2004	£20,000 (net of VAT)
Estimated life	4 years
Estimated production:	
2004	55,000 units
2005	50,000 units
2006	40,000 units
2007	35,000 units
Estimated scrap value at 31 December 2007	£2,000 (net of VAT)

The accountant is unsure whether to depreciate the machine using:

• the straight-line method

• the units of output method

She asks you to calculate the depreciation amounts for each year using the two methods. (Note: the company's financial year end is 31 December.)

Explain whether the depreciation amounts will be listed as direct expenses or indirect expenses.

4.6   The production manager of 'Print 'n Go', a specialist short-run printing business, is considering the purchase of a new computer-linked scanner. The cost is likely to be £18,000 (net of VAT) and the scanner will have a life of approximately four years, after which it will have a trade-in value of between £2,000 and £2,500 (net of VAT). The production manager knows from past experience that such equipment has the most use, and will lose most value, in the early part of its life.

As an accounts assistant you are to write a memorandum (on the next page) to the production manager detailing:

• the method of depreciation that could be used

• an approximate rate that could be applied, showing appropriate workings

• reasons for the choice of depreciation method

MEMORANDUM

To:

From:

Date:

4.7 Greenacres Limited manufactures two types of garden lawnmower – the 'Alpha', an electric mower, and the 'Beta', a petrol mower. The general expenses account for the month ended 30 November 2004 has a debit balance of £34,500. This balance is analysed as:

		£
•	direct expenses – Alpha	8,390
•	direct expenses – Beta	6,240
•	production overheads	13,850
•	non-production overheads – selling and distribution	3,170
•	non-production overheads – administration	2,850
		34,500

The following cost accounting codes are in use to record expenses:

code number	description
1500	work-in-progress: Alpha
1600	work-in-progress: Beta
2000	production overheads
2500	non-production overheads: selling and distribution
2600	non-production overheads: administration
3000	general expenses

As an accounts assistant at Greenacres Limited you have been given the following tasks:

Task 1

Prepare general expenses account for the month ended 30 November 2004:

Dr		General Expenses Account		Cr
2004		£	2004	£
30 Nov	Balance b/d	34,500		

Task 2

Complete the following table to show how the total cost of general expenses is split between work-in-progress, production overheads and non-production overheads.

2004	Code	Debit	Credit
30 Nov	1500		
30 Nov	3000		
30 Nov	1600		
30 Nov	3000		
30 Nov	2000		
30 Nov	3000		
30 Nov	2500		
30 Nov	3000		
30 Nov	2600		
30 Nov	3000		

4.8 In the graphs below, draw in the lines to show how fixed costs and variable costs behave with changes in the level of activity.

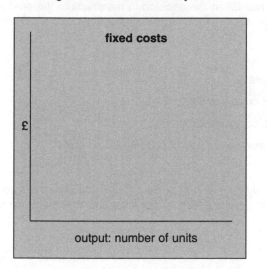

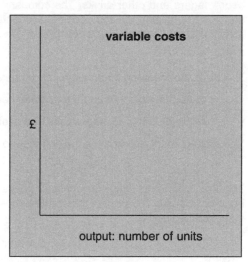

4.9 Classify the following costs (tick the appropriate column):

		FIXED	SEMI-VARIABLE	VARIABLE
(a)	rent of business premises			
(b)	week's hire of machinery at £100 per week for one particular job			
(c)	photocopier with a fixed rental and a cost per unit			
(d)	supervisor's wages			
(e)	reducing balance depreciation			
(f)	production-line employees paid a basic wage, with a bonus linked to output			
(g)	royalty paid to author for each book sold			
(h)	accountant's fees			
(i)	raw materials used in production process			

4.10 The research and development department of Castlemayne Limited, a design and engineering business, has recently developed a new type of electronic dispenser for serving exact quantities of beers, lagers and other drinks. The company has taken the decision to manufacture the product and you are helping the management accountant to prepare budgeted production costs at different levels of output of the new dispenser.

You have the following information in front of you:

- at 20,000 units of output, total budgeted costs are £350,000

- at 30,000 units of output, total budgeted costs are £500,000

The development manager has telephoned to ask the amount of budgeted fixed costs.

You are to use the 'high/low' technique to identify the element of fixed costs. You know from your involvement with the project that variable costs have a linear relationship, and that there are no stepped fixed costs.

4.11 David Khan is a motor vehicle engineer who has designed a fuel pump which gives cars greater fuel economy. He has decided to set up in business to manufacture the product and has carried out market research which suggests that demand for the product will be between 12,000 and 20,000 units each year.

David has budgeted the production costs on the basis of an output of 12,000 units as follows:

			£
variable costs	–	materials	36,000
	–	labour	24,000
	–	expenses	6,000
fixed costs	–	labour	18,500
	–	overheads	25,250

David asks you to prepare a schedule of budgeted production costs based on outputs of 12,000 units, 15,000 units and 20,000 units each year. The schedule is to show total production cost and the cost per unit at each level of output. (Note: you may assume that there is a linear relationship for variable costs, and that there are no stepped fixed costs.)

Briefly describe and explain the trend in costs per unit for the three budgeted levels of production.

5 OVERHEADS

5.1 Mereford Management College is a private college that has two teaching departments – accountancy and management.

The College charges overheads on the basis of lecturer hours. The following overhead analysis information is available to you (note that support services overheads – such as the administration office, reprographics department and learning resources – have already been apportioned to the teaching departments):

OVERHEAD ANALYSIS SHEET for January 2004	Accountancy Department	Management Department
Budgeted total overheads (£)	22,143	17,251
Budgeted lecturer hours	1,525	1,300
Budgeted overhead absorption rate (£)		

Details of a particular course – 'Finance for Managers' – that is taught in both the accountancy and management departments are as follows:

OVERHEAD ANALYSIS SHEET Course: Finance for Managers	Accountancy Department	Management Department
Lecturer hours	45	20
Budgeted overhead absorption rate (£)		
Overhead absorbed by course (£)		

You are to:

(a) calculate the overhead absorption rate for each of the two departments and complete the overhead analysis sheet

(b) calculate the overhead absorbed by the 'Finance for Managers' course and complete the course overhead analysis sheet

(c) suggest an alternative overhead absorption rate that the College might use and comment on the circumstances that would make it appropriate

5.2 Wyevale Processing Limited processes and packs fruit and vegetables for supermarkets. The company has five departments – processing, packing, quality assurance, stores and maintenance.

The cost accountant has given you an overhead analysis schedule (see next page) to complete for next month.

The following information is available:

	Processing	Packing	Quality Assurance	Stores	Maintenance
Floor area (square metres)	160	210	50	80	100
Employees (number)	10	14	2	2	2
Machine usage (hours)	300	100	40		
Materials requisitions (number)	50	60	12		5
Maintenance hours (number)	60	50	20		

You are to:

(a) Prepare an analysis of budgeted production overheads for next month showing the basis of apportionment to the five departments of the business.

(b) Outline what now needs to be done with the budgeted costs of the service departments in order to arrive at overhead absorption rates for the production departments. Explain the reasons for this action.

5.3 Mercia Metals Limited is a manufacturing company with three production cost centres: forging, stamping and finishing. The following are the expected factory expenses for the forthcoming year:

	£
Rent and rates	14,625
Depreciation of machinery	8,000
Insurance of machinery	680
Supervisory salaries	42,790
Heating and lighting	4,420

Cost centre information is:

	Forging	Stamping	Finishing
Floor area (sq m)	400	600	300
Value of machinery	£30,000	£40,000	£10,000
Number of production-line employees	4	5	2

You are to:

(a) Apportion the expenses to the cost centres, stating the basis of apportionment.

(b) Calculate the overhead absorption rate (to two decimal places) of each cost centre, based on direct labour hours. Note that the company works a 35-hour week for 48 weeks a year.

BUDGETED PRODUCTION OVERHEAD SCHEDULE
for next month

Overhead	Basis of apportionment	Total £	Processing £	Packing £	Quality Assurance £	Stores £	Maintenance £
Rent and rates		4,500					
Supervisory salaries		3,690					
Depreciation of machinery		2,640					
Canteen costs		360					
TOTAL		11,190					

5.4 Wyvern Private Hospital plc has two patient wards – a day care ward for minor operations where the patients go home at the end of the day, and a surgical ward for patients who remain in the hospital for several days. There are two service departments – the operating theatre and administration.

The overheads of each department for last month were as follows:

	£
• day care ward	28,750
• surgical ward	42,110
• operating theatre	32,260
• administration	9,075

The basis for re-apportioning the overheads of the service departments is:

- operating theatre, on the number of operations carried out – day care ward, 160; surgical ward, 120

- administration, on the number of staff in each department – day care ward, 10; surgical ward, 25; operating theatre, 20

You are to use the step-down method to re-apportion the two service department overheads to the two patient wards.

5.5 Fox Furniture Limited makes tables and chairs for school and college use. There are two production lines – tables, and chairs – and two service departments – stores and maintenance.

The overheads of each department for last month were as follows:

	£
• tables	12,000
• chairs	8,000
• stores	3,000
• maintenance	2,000

The basis for re-apportioning the overheads of the service departments is:

- stores, on the number of requisitions – tables, 100; chairs, 80; maintenance, 20

- maintenance, on the value of equipment in each department – tables, £30,000; chairs, £20,000

You are to use the step-down method to re-apportion the two service department overheads to the two production departments.

5.6 Steel Forgings (Rowcester) Limited is a heavy engineering business making parts for the car industry. The factory works a 35-hour week and is divided into three manufacturing divisions, with each making a different type of steel forging. Details of last week's production are as follows:

	Division 1	Division 2	Division 3
Direct materials	£3,260	£4,940	£8,760
Direct labour	£1,810	£2,525	£2,850
Number of production-line employees	5	8	10
Number of machine hours	150	250	300
Number of units produced	2,000	2,500	1,000

Production overheads were £10,000 for last week.

You are to:

(a) suggest two different methods by which overheads can be absorbed, and calculate the appropriate overhead absorption rates

(b) calculate the production cost per unit of output in each division using the two different methods of overhead absorption

(c) compare the results of your calculations and suggest the most appropriate method of overhead absorption for this business

Note: where appropriate, round answers to the nearest penny

5.7 Jean-E-Us Limited manufactures denim jeans that are sold to various clothing retailers. The company's operations are organised by departments, as follows:

- Warehouse
- Manufacturing
- Sales
- Accounting

The budgeted and actual fixed overheads of the company for the four weeks ended 27 October 2004 were as follows:

	£
Depreciation of fixed assets	5,000
Rent	6,000
Other property overheads	4,000
Accounting overheads	2,500
Staff costs:	
– warehouse	4,600
– indirect manufacturing	10,500
– sales	7,340
– accounting	3,250
Total budgeted and actual fixed overheads	43,190

The following information is also relevant:

Department	% of floor space occupied	Net book value of fixed assets £000
Warehouse	30%	100
Manufacturing	40%	300
Sales	20%	50
Accounting	10%	50
	100%	500

Overheads are allocated and apportioned between departments using the most appropriate basis.

Task 1

Please see next page.

Task 2

Manufacturing fixed overheads are absorbed on the basis of budgeted machine hours. The budgeted number of machine hours for the four weeks ended 27 October 2004 was 2,000 hours.

You are to calculate the budgeted fixed overhead absorption rate for the manufacturing department for the period.

5.8   Milestone Motors Limited sells and services cars. The company's operations are organised into three profit centres and one cost centre, as follows:

Profit centres
- New car sales
- Used car sales
- Servicing

Cost centre
- Administration

The budgeted and actual fixed overheads of the company for the four weeks ended 28 April 2004 were as follows:

	£
Depreciation of fixed assets	8,400
Rent	10,000
Other property overheads	4,500
Staff costs:	
– new car sales	11,080
– used car sales	7,390
– servicing	9,975
– administration	6,850
Administration overheads	3,860
Total budgeted and actual fixed overheads	62,055

continued on page 40

Activity 5.7: Task 1

Complete the following table showing:

- the basis for allocation or apportionment of each overhead
- the allocation and apportionment of fixed overheads between the four departments

Fixed overheads for four weeks ended 27 October 2004	Basis	Total £	Warehouse £	Manufacturing £	Sales £	Accounting £
Depreciation		5,000				
Rent		6,000				
Other property overheads		4,000				
Accounting overheads		2,500				
Staff costs		25,690				
		43,190				

The following information is also relevant:

Profit/Cost centre	% of floor space occupied	Net book value of fixed assets £000
New car sales	40%	50
Used car sales	30%	30
Servicing	20%	100
Administration	10%	20
	100%	200

Overheads are allocated and apportioned using the most appropriate basis. The total administration overheads are then re-apportioned to the three profit centres using the following percentages.

- New car sales   20%
- Used car sales   30%
- Servicing   50%

Task 1

Please see next page.

Task 2

Servicing centre fixed overheads are absorbed on the basis of budgeted direct labour hours. The budgeted number of direct labour hours for the servicing centre during the four weeks ended 28 April 2004 was 1,025 hours.

You are to calculate the budgeted fixed overhead absorption rate per direct labour hour for the servicing centre during the period.

5.9   Garden Cottage Limited manufactures 'homestyle' soups which are sold through supermarkets and convenience stores. The soups pass through two departments – kitchen and canning. Details of overheads for the departments for the four weeks ended 16 June 2004 are as follows:

Kitchen Department

- overhead absorption rate is £7.00 per direct labour hour
- direct labour hours worked were 800
- actual cost of production overhead was £5,000

Canning Department

- overhead absorption rate is £8.00 per machine hour
- machine hours worked were 400
- actual cost of production overhead was £3,500

continued on page 42

Activity 5.8: Task 1

Complete the following table showing:

- the basis for allocation or apportionment of each overhead;
- the allocation and apportionment of fixed overheads between the four centres;
- the re-apportionment of the total administration overheads.

Fixed overheads for four weeks ended 28 April 2004	Basis	Total £	New Car Sales £	Used Car Sales £	Servicing £	Administration £
Depreciation of fixed assets		8,400				
Rent		10,000				
Other property overheads		4,500				
Staff costs		35,295				
Administration overheads		3,860				
		62,055				( )
Administration		62,055				–

The following cost accounting codes are in use to record overheads:

code number	description
2000	work-in-progress
2100	production overheads: kitchen department
2200	production overheads: canning department
4000	profit and loss account

As an accounts assistant at Garden Cottage Limited, you are asked to prepare the two production overheads accounts below and to fill in the table as at 16 June 2004 to account for the overheads and the over- and under-absorption of overheads.

Dr **Production Overheads Account: Kitchen Department** Cr

2004	£	2004	£

Dr **Production Overheads Account: Canning Department** Cr

2004	£	2004	£

2004	Code	Debit	Credit

6 METHODS OF COSTING

6.1 Wyvern Engineers Limited is a company which specialises in making parts for the car industry. The following Job Cost Sheet has been prepared by you, the Accounting Technician, for the actual costs of manufacture of a batch of gearbox casings for Mawgam Cars, a local specialist builder of touring cars:

		ACTUAL COSTS
2004	**JOB NO 471/99** **for gearbox casings** **Customer: Mawgam Cars**	**£**
	Direct Materials	
8 Sep	MR 3141	422
10 Sep	MR 3152	286
10 Sep	MRN 58	(145)
	Direct Labour	
10 Sep	Wages analysis (30 hours)	420
	Direct Expenses	
8 Sep	Engineer's fee	250
	Production Overheads	345
	TOTAL COST	1,578

Note: Wyvern Engineers uses a labour hour rate for absorbing production overheads.

Your assistant asks you to explain the following about the Job Cost Sheet:

(a)   What does the transaction 'MR 3141' on 8 September mean?

(b)   What does the transaction 'MRN 58' on 10 September mean?

(c)   Where has the information on direct labour hours come from?

(d)   Why is the engineer's fee shown as a direct expense?

(e)   What is the absorption rate for production overheads?

6.2 OB Printers has been asked by John Dun, a local poet, to quote for the cost of printing a small book of poetry. John Dun is not sure how many copies to order, and has asked for quotations for 500, 1,000 and 2,000 copies.

The estimates by OB Printers are as follows:

Setting up the printing machine:	6 hours at £10.00 per hour
Artwork:	7 hours at £12.00 per hour
Typesetting:	20 hours at £15.00 per hour
Paper (for 500 copies):	£100.00
Other printing consumables (for 500 copies):	£50.00
Direct labour (for 500 copies):	5 hours at £13.00 per hour
Production overheads:	80% of direct labour costs
Profit:	25% on cost price

You are to:

(a) prepare the Job Cost Sheet (see next page) for 500, 1,000 and 2,000 copies, and also show the selling prices

(b) calculate the cost per book (to the nearest penny) to the author at each of the three different production levels

(c) respond to John Dun who, on seeing the quotations, says:

"Why is the price per copy so high for 500 copies? I am a starving poet, and I can't afford to have a large quantity printed. If the book sells well I shall regret not having had 2,000 copies printed."

JOB NO 12345

Poetry book for John Dun

	NUMBER OF COPIES		
	500	1,000	2,000
	£	£	£
Fixed Costs			
Setting up machine			
Artwork			
Typesetting			
Direct Materials			
Paper			
Other printing consumables			
Direct Labour			
Production Overheads			
TOTAL COST			
Profit (25% of total cost)			
SELLING PRICE			

6.3 A manufacturer of security alarms has the following information concerning the first month of production:

	£
direct materials	10,725
direct labour	6,600
production overheads	3,900
security alarms completed	2,750
security alarms in progress	500

The work-in-progress is complete as regards materials, but is 50% complete as regards direct labour and production overheads.

You are to:

(a) complete the schedule below in order to calculate the cost per security alarm for the first month's production

(b) calculate the month-end valuation for work-in-progress

Note: use the average cost basis for your calculations

Cost element	Costs	Completed Units	Work-in-progress			Total Equivalent Units	Cost per Unit	WIP valuation
			Units	% complete	Equivalent Units			
	A	B	C	D	E	F	G	H
	£				C x D	B + E	A ÷ F	E x G
							£	£
Direct materials								
Direct labour								
Production overheads								
Total								

6.4 Rowcester Limited makes 'older style' radios. At the beginning of January, following demand from shops over the Christmas period, there is no opening work-in-progress.

. The costs of production during January were as follows:

	£
direct materials	98,500
direct labour	43,645
production overheads	50,525

At the end of January, 18,000 radios had been completed, and 7,000 radios remained in progress. The closing work-in-progress was complete as regards direct materials, and 50% complete as regards direct labour and overheads.

You are to complete the schedule below in order to:

(a) calculate the cost per radio for completed output in January

(b) calculate the value of work-in-progress at the end of January

Note: use the average cost basis for your calculations

Cost element	Costs	Completed Units	Work-in-progress			Total Equivalent Units	Cost per Unit	WIP valuation
			Units	% complete	Equivalent Units			
	A	B	C	D	E	F	G	H
					C x D	B + E	A ÷ F	E x G
	£						£	£
Direct materials								
Direct labour								
Production overheads								
Total								

6.5 Wyvern Chemicals Limited produces a chemical, which is made in one production process.

For the four weeks ended 9 April 2004, the company input 65,000 litres of direct materials, had an output of 60,000 litres and a normal loss of 5,000 litres. The input costs were: materials £19,500, labour £13,000, overheads £9,750. Normal losses were sold to a specialist reprocessing company for 5p per litre.

There was no opening or closing stock at the beginning and end of the process; all output was complete.

As an accounts assistant, you are to prepare the process account and the normal loss account for the four weeks ended 9 April 2004.

6.6   Hawke Limited produces a washing powder called 'CleanO', which is made in one production process.

For the four weeks ended 24 September 2004, the company input 84,000 kilos of direct materials, had an output of 81,000 kilos – the difference of 3,000 kilos was made up of a normal loss of 4,000 kilos and an abnormal gain of 1,000 kilos.

The input costs were: materials £16,800, labour £12,600, overheads £4,200. All losses were sold to a specialist reprocessing company for 20p per kilo.

There was no opening or closing stock at the beginning and end of the process; all output was complete.

As an accounts assistant, you are to prepare the process account, the abnormal gain account, and the normal loss account for the four weeks ended 24 September 2004.

6.7   Burncoose Limited is a manufacturer of vitamin tablets. Its best-selling product, called 'Vita', is made in two production processes before completion and transfer to finished goods stock.

For the four weeks ended 16 July 2004, details of production of 'Vita' were as follows:

	Process 1	*Process 2*
Direct materials (5,000 kilos)	£2,000	–
Labour	£1,000	£1,125
Overhead	£500	£675
Normal loss in process of input	5%	3%
Output	4,500 kilos	4,400 kilos
Scrap value of all losses	£0.20 per kilo	£0.40 per kilo

There was no opening or closing stock at the beginning and end of either process; all output was complete. All losses were sold to a specialist reprocessing company.

As an accounts assistant, you are to prepare the following accounts for the four weeks ended 16 July 2004:

• process 1 account

• process 2 account

• normal loss account

• abnormal loss account

• abnormal gain account

Note: calculate costs per unit of expected output to the nearest penny.

7 BOOK-KEEPING FOR COSTING

7.1 In a manufacturing account, indirect materials and indirect labour form part of:

    (a)   prime cost

    (b)   production overheads

    (c)   non-production overheads

    (d)   indirect expenses

    Answer (a) or (b) or (c) or (d)

7.2 Allocate the following costs (tick the appropriate column):

	manufacturing account	profit and loss account
(a) salaries of sales staff		
(b) wages of production-line employees		
(c) royalty paid to designer of product		
(d) straight-line depreciation of factory machinery		
(e) factory power costs		
(f) re-decoration of administration offices		
(g) units of service depreciation of photocopier in administration office		
(h) bank overdraft interest		
(i) overtime paid to production-line employees		

7.3 The following figures relate to the accounts of Middleton Manufacturing Limited for the year ended 31 December 2004:

	£
Stocks at 1 January 2004:	
Raw materials	25,250
Finished goods	12,380
Stocks at 31 December 2004:	
Raw materials	29,610
Finished goods	11,490
Expenditure during year:	
Purchases of raw materials	75,340
Factory wages – direct	54,690
Factory wages – indirect	22,330
Factory rent and rates	7,380
Factory power	4,250
Depreciation of factory machinery	2,500
Factory maintenance	1,870
Sundry factory expenses	1,140
Non-production overheads	46,730
Sales of finished goods	286,940

Note: Factory power is to be treated as a production overhead.

You are to prepare the year-end:

* manufacturing account
* profit and loss account

Note: please see the Appendix (page 288) for specimen formats of a manufacturing account and a profit and loss account.

7.4 The following figures relate to the accounts of Ryedale Limited, a manufacturing business, for the year ended 31 October 2004:

	£
Stocks of raw materials at 1 November 2003	41,210
Stocks of raw materials, 31 October 2004	46,380
Stocks of finished goods, 1 November 2003	29,470
Stocks of finished goods, 31 October 2004	38,290
Purchases of raw materials	311,050
Sales of finished goods	874,360
Rent and rates	35,640
Factory wages – direct	180,860
Factory wages – indirect	45,170
Factory power	12,040
Factory heat and light	5,030
Factory sundry expenses and maintenance	10,390
Administration salaries	154,610
Advertising	30,780
Office expenses	10,390
Depreciation of factory plant and machinery	12,500
Depreciation of office equipment	2,500

Additional information:

- factory power is to be treated as a production overhead
- rent and rates are to be allocated 75% to manufacturing and 25% to administration

You are to prepare the year-end:

- manufacturing account
- profit and loss account

Note: please see the Appendix (page 288) for specimen formats of a manufacturing account and a profit and loss account.

7.5 Shah and Company is a manufacturing business which uses an integrated book-keeping system for its costing and financial accounting.

At 1 January 2004, the first day of a new financial year, the company has a number of balances in its ledger as shown on the next few pages.

During January the following transactions took place:

	£
Direct materials bought on credit	12,500
Direct labour costs paid by cheque	10,500
Production overheads paid by cheque	4,000
Non-production overheads paid by cheque	5,000
Credit sales	38,000
Receipts from debtors	41,000
Paid to creditors	12,000
Direct materials transferred to work-in-progress	13,000
Work-in-progress transferred to finished goods	28,000
Finished goods transferred to cost of sales	27,000

You are to:

(a) Record the above transactions in the integrated book-keeping system of Shah and Company, using the accounts on the next four pages, and show the net profit for the month. (Note that the full cost of direct labour and production overheads is to be transferred to work-in-progress.)

(b) Show the trial balance at 31 January 2004, after preparing the profit and loss account in the double-entry accounts.

Dr		Capital Account			Cr
2004			£	2004		£
				1 Jan	Balance b/d	40,000

Dr		Machinery Account			Cr
2004			£	2004		£
1 Jan	Balance b/d	15,000				

Dr		Office Equipment Account			Cr
2004			£	2004		£
1 Jan	Balance b/d	8,000				

Dr		Bank Account			Cr
2004			£	2004		£
1 Jan	Balance b/d	5,500				

Dr		Materials Account		Cr
2004		£	2004	£
1 Jan	Balance b/d	3,500		

Dr		Work-in-Progress Account		Cr
2004		£	2004	£
1 Jan	Balance b/d	3,000		

Dr		Finished Goods Account		Cr
2004		£	2004	£
1 Jan	Balance b/d	4,000		

Dr		Debtors' Account		Cr
2004		£	2004	£
1 Jan	Balance b/d	5,000		

Dr			**Creditors' Account**		Cr
2004			£	2004	£
				1 Jan Balance b/d	4,000

Dr		**Labour Costs Account**		Cr
2004	£	2004		£

Dr		**Production Overheads Account**		Cr
2004	£	2004		£

Dr		**Non-Production Overheads Account**		Cr
2004	£	2004		£

Dr		Sales Account		Cr
2004	£	2004		£

Dr		Cost of Sales Account		Cr
2004	£	2004		£

Dr		Profit and Loss Account		Cr
2004	£	2004		£

7.6   Albion Limited, a manufacturing company, has three departments – moulding, assembly and finishing. The company uses a budgeted overhead absorption rate based on direct labour hours.

The following data relates to production week 46:

	Moulding Department	Assembly Department	Finishing Department
Actual overheads incurred	£1,246	£2,021	£912
Budgeted absorption rate per direct labour hour	£10.40	£12.80	£9.50
Actual direct labour hours worked	125	155	96
Overhead absorbed			
(Under-)/over-absorption of overheads			

You are to complete for each department:

(a)   the table (above) to show the amount of overhead absorbed and the under- or over-absorption of overheads

(b)   the production overheads accounts (below), including any transfer to profit and loss account

Dr	**Production Overheads Account: Moulding Department**		Cr
	£		£
Bank (overheads incurred)	1,246		

Dr	**Production Overheads Account: Assembly Department**		Cr
	£		£
Bank (overheads incurred)	2,021		

Dr	**Production Overheads Account: Finishing Department**		Cr
	£		£
Bank (overheads incurred)	912		

(c)   What effect will this under- or over-absorption have on budgeted profits?

7.7   The data which follows relates to the finishing department of Bringsty Manufacturing. In this department overheads are recovered on the basis of machine hours.

Finishing Department Period ending 30 June 1999	
Budgeted overhead	£109,931
Budgeted machine hours	10,550
Budgeted overhead absorption rate	
Actual machine hours	10,350
Overhead absorbed	
Actual overhead	£114,592
(Under-)/over-absorption of overhead	

As an accounts assistant you are to:

(a)   Complete the table above

(b)   Write a memorandum to the Accountant which explains:

- the consequences of the results for the period

- the possible causes

- the effect on the costing of jobs which passed through the finishing department during the period

- possible action to be taken for the future

7.8   Wye (Horticultural) Limited produces a liquid fertiliser for garden flowers called 'GreenGrow', which is made in one production process.

For the four weeks ended 22 October 2004, the company input 22,000 litres of direct materials, and had an output of 20,400 litres – the difference of 1,600 litres was made up of a normal loss of 2,000 litres and an abnormal gain of 400 litres.

The input costs were: materials £11,000, labour £7,700, overheads £5,500. All losses were sold to a specialist reprocessing company for 10p per litre.

There was no opening or closing stock at the beginning and end of the process; all output was complete.

As an accounts assistant, you are to prepare the process account, the abnormal gain account, and the normal loss account for the four weeks ended 22 October 2004.

7.9 Goonvrea Limited manufactures a chemical, 'Maravose', within two separate processes. For the week-ended 17 September 2004 the details were:

- *Process 1*

    – materials input, 4,000 kilos at £5 per kilo

    – labour, £4,360

    – overheads, £2,960

- *Process 2*

    – materials input, 3,500 kilos at £4 per kilo

    – labour, £2,640

    – overheads, £1,790

Normal outputs are:

- Process 1, 95% of input

- Process 2, 90% of input

All losses are sold at a scrap value of £0.75 per kilo to a specialist reprocessing company.

There was no work-in-progress at either the beginning or end of the week.

Output during the week was 3,700 kilos from Process 1 and 6,600 kilos from Process 2.

As an accounts assistant at Goonvrea Limited you are asked to prepare the process 1 account, process 2 account, normal loss account, abnormal loss account, and the abnormal gain account for the week ended 17 September 2004. Note: calculate costs per unit of expected output to the nearest penny.

8 SHORT-TERM DECISIONS

8.1 Bert Peters is the owner of a petrol filling station which has the following weekly costs:

Cost of petrol from oil company	80p per litre
Selling price	85p per litre
Fixed overheads	£750

You are to:

- Prepare a table showing costs, sales revenue, and profit or loss for sale of petrol in multiples of 1,000 litres up to 20,000 litres.

- If sales are currently 18,000 litres each week, what is the margin of safety, expressed as a percentage and in litres?

8.2 Kings B & B is a bed and breakfast establishment that caters for individual travellers who want a good night's sleep in a clean bed with a hearty breakfast. There are 10 single bedrooms available, and bed and breakfast is priced at £22 per person per night. Kings B & B is open 7 nights a week.

The following are typical costs:

	weekly costs (for the whole place) £	costs per guest night £
Heating and lighting	42	
Breakfast food		4
Cleaning staff – basic pay	100	
Cleaning staff – bonus		2
Administration	90	
Laundry		3
Breakfast staff	72	
Other overheads	60	

You are to:

(a) Calculate the fixed costs per week and the contribution per guest per night.

(b) Calculate the number of guests per night it would take to break-even.

(c) Calculate the weekly profit or loss if there were 42 guest nights in a week (ie an average of 6 guests on each of the 7 nights).

8.3   Peter Parkinson is a central heating engineer who has designed a special type of thermostatic valve for use in heating systems. He has decided to set up in business to manufacture the product and he has carried out market research which suggests that demand for the product will be between 9,000 units and 20,000 units each year. Accordingly he has produced the following forecasts at different levels of production and sales:

sales (number of units)	9,000	12,000	15,000	20,000
direct materials	£27,000	£36,000	£45,000	£60,000
direct labour	£9,000	£12,000	£15,000	£20,000
production overheads	£66,000	£72,000	£78,000	£88,000

Each thermostatic valve will sell for £10.

Peter asks you to help him interpret the results, and in particular he wishes to know:

(a)   the profit or loss he will make at each level of production

(b)   the break-even point

(c)   the fixed amount of production overheads

One market research survey suggested that a sales level of 30,000 units each year might be achieved. In the form of a report, you, as an accounts assistant, are to:

•   rework the forecast at this sales level and calculate the net profit or loss which will be achieved

•   advise Peter Parkinson of any limitations and the usefulness of your figures at this level of production

8.4   Wyvern Porcelain Limited produces decorated porcelain figures which are sold in quality shops both in the UK and abroad. The figures are especially popular with holidaymakers from other countries who visit the factory and see the figures being made.

There are three ranges of porcelain figures – 'people', 'animals' and 'birds'. The expected monthly costs and sales information for each range is as follows:

Product	'People'	'Animals'	'Birds'
Sales and production units*	1,000	2,000	2,700
Labour hours per month	1,500	1,000	900
Total sales revenue	£60,000	£55,000	£47,250
Total direct materials	£5,000	£6,000	£5,400
Total direct labour	£15,000	£10,000	£9,000
Total variable overheads	£10,000	£9,000	£8,000

* note: a unit is a porcelain figure

The total expected monthly fixed costs relating to the production of all porcelain figures are £45,400.

As an accounts assistant at Wyvern Porcelain Limited, you are to carry out the following tasks.

Task 1

Complete the table below to show for each product range the expected contribution per unit.

Product	'People' £	'Animals' £	'Birds' £
Selling price per unit			
Less: Unit variable costs			
Direct materials			
Direct labour			
Variable overheads			
Contribution per unit			

Task 2

If the company only produces the 'People' range, calculate the number of units it would need to make and sell each month to cover the fixed costs of £45,400.

Task 3

Making and painting the porcelain figures are highly skilled tasks, and unskilled labour cannot be brought in to cover for absent staff.

Unfortunately, because of staff illness, the available labour hours are reduced from 3,400 to 2,800. The finance director asks you to calculate the contribution of each unit (porcelain figure) per labour hour.

Using the data from Task 1, complete the table below.

Product	'People'	'Animals'	'Birds'
Contribution per unit			
Labour hours per unit			
Contribution per labour hour			

Task 4

Using the data from Task 3, calculate how many units of each of product ranges 'People', 'Animals' and 'Birds' the company should make and sell in order to maximise its profits using 2,800 labour hours.

8.5 Mercia Airways is a local airline which flies to short-haul destinations within the UK and Europe. The costs of weekly flight MA 005 to Rome, which uses a 100 seater aircraft are as follows:

direct materials	£12.50 per passenger
direct labour	£10.00 per passenger
direct expenses	£2.50 per passenger
fixed overheads	£3,500 per flight

For next week's flight, sixty seats have been sold at a standard-class fare of £100 each.

You are to calculate:

- the absorption cost per seat on this flight with sixty seats sold

- the marginal cost per seat

- the profit or loss if no further tickets are sold for this flight

The Marketing Manager thinks it unlikely that any further standard-class fares will be sold. There are two possibilities that she must consider:

- to release the surplus seats to a firm that sells cheap flights: the airline will receive £45 for each seat sold and, from past experience, the marketing manager expects thirty seats to be sold

- to sell all forty spare seats to a local newspaper, which will offer them as prizes for a 'spot-the-ball' competition: the newspaper will pay £35 per seat

As an accounts assistant, you are to write a memorandum to the Marketing Manager, advising whether either of these possibilities should be considered; explain your reasoning, and illustrate your answer with profit statements.

8.6 The Last Company is famous for its 'Snowdon' range of hill-walking boots. The management of the company is considering the production for next year and has asked for help with certain financial decisions.

The following information is available:

wholesale selling price (per pair)	£60
direct materials (per pair)	£20
direct labour (per pair)	£18
fixed overheads	£200,000 per year

The company is planning to manufacture 12,500 pairs of boots next year.

You are to calculate:

- the absorption cost per pair

- the marginal cost per pair

- the profit or loss if 12,500 pairs of boots are sold

A mail order company, Sales-by-Post Limited, has approached The Last Company with a view to selling the 'Snowdon' boot through its catalogue. Sales-by-Post offers two contracts:

- either 2,500 pairs of boots at £45 per pair

- or 5,000 pairs of boots at £37 per pair

As The Last Company usually sells through specialist shops, it is not expected that 'normal' sales will be affected. These 'special orders' are within the capacity of the factory, and fixed overheads will remain unchanged.

As an accounts assistant, you are to write a memorandum to the Managing Director advising her whether these offers should be accepted; illustrate your answer with profit statements.

8.7   Tempus Limited makes reproduction antique clocks. The company produces 2,500 clocks each year and the costs per unit of output are:

	£
direct materials	20.50
direct labour	31.00
variable production overheads	5.50
fixed production overheads	4.00
fixed non-production overheads	3.00
	64.00

The selling price of each clock is £80.00

The Managing Director of the business, Jane Haslam, has been thinking about how to increase profits for next year. She has asked you, as an accounts assistant, to look at the following two proposals from a cost accounting viewpoint.

Proposal 1

To reduce the selling price of each clock to £70.00. This is expected to increase sales by 1,000 clocks each year to a total of 3,500 clocks. Apart from changes in variable costs, there would be no change in fixed costs.

Proposal 2

To increase the selling price of each clock to £100.00. This is expected to reduce sales by 500 clocks each year to a total of 2,000 clocks. Apart from changes in variable costs, there would be a reduction of £3,000 in fixed production overheads.

You are to write a memorandum to Jane Haslam, the Managing Director, stating your advice, giving reasons and workings. Each of the two proposals is to be considered on its own merits without reference to the other proposal.

8.8 Durning Limited manufactures one product, the Durn. For the month of April 2004 the following information is available:

number of units manufactured	10,000
number of units sold	8,000
selling price	£4 per unit
direct materials for month	£8,000
direct labour for month	£16,000
fixed production overheads for month	£10,000

There was no finished goods stock at the start of the month. Both direct materials and direct labour behave as variable costs.

You are to:

(a) produce profit statements for April 2004, using:

• marginal costing

• absorption costing

(b) explain briefly the reason for the difference between recorded profits under the alternative costing systems

9 LONG-TERM DECISIONS

TABLE OF DISCOUNTED CASH FLOW FACTORS

Cost of capital/ rate of return	10%	12%	14%	16%	18%	20%	22%	24%
Year 1	0.909	0.893	0.877	0.862	0.847	0.833	0.820	0.806
Year 2	0.826	0.797	0.769	0.743	0.718	0.694	0.672	0.650
Year 3	0.751	0.712	0.675	0.641	0.609	0.579	0.551	0.524
Year 4	0.683	0.636	0.592	0.552	0.516	0.482	0.451	0.423
Year 5	0.621	0.567	0.519	0.476	0.437	0.402	0.370	0.341
Year 6	0.564	0.507	0.456	0.410	0.370	0.335	0.303	0.275

Tutorial note: In Skills Tests and Examinations you will always be given the appropriate factors.

9.1 The following information relates to two major capital investment projects being considered by Newell Limited. For financial reasons, only one project can be accepted.

		Project Ess	Project Tee
		£	£
Initial cost at the beginning of the project		100,000	115,000
Net cash inflows, year:	1	40,000	50,000
	2	60,000	35,000
	3	20,000	30,000
	4	20,000	30,000
	5	10,000	30,000
Expected scrap value at end of year 5		5,000	7,500

The initial cost occurs at the beginning of the project and you may assume that the net cash inflows will arise at the end of each year. Newell Limited requires an annual rate of return of 10 per cent.

To help the Managing Director of Newell Limited make her decision, as accounts assistant you are to:

- produce numerical assessments of the two projects based on the following capital investment appraisal methods:
  - (a) the payback period
  - (b) the net present value

- write a report to the Managing Director on the relative merits of the project appraisal methods, and advise her which capital investment, if either, should be undertaken

9.2   A capital investment project has the following expected cash flows over its life of three years:

	£
Initial cost at the beginning of the project	(55,000)
Net cash inflows, year: 1	19,376
2	28,491
3	21,053

The expected scrap value at the end of year 3 is nil.

You are to:

(a)   Calculate the net present value of the project at annual rates of return of 10 per cent, 12 per cent and 14 per cent. Calculate all money amounts to the nearest £.

(b)   What do your calculations in part (a) tell you about this project?

9.3   You work as an accounts assistant for the Chester Carpet Company, which makes quality carpets. Currently you are working on the appraisal of a capital investment project to purchase a new machine for the production department in December 2004.

The machine will cost £65,000 and will have a useful life of four years. The cash inflows are expected to be:

	£
2005	17,000
2006	25,000
2007	31,000
2008	24,000

At the end of the project, the machine will be sold as scrap for an expected amount of £4,000.

Chester Carpet Company requires an annual rate of return of 10 per cent for net present value, and a maximum payback period of three years.

Task 1

Use the working paper on the next page to calculate the net present value and the payback period of the proposed project. Ignore inflation and calculate all money amounts to the nearest £.

Task 2

Write a report, dated 24 November 2004, to the General Manager evaluating the proposal from a financial viewpoint. State any assumptions you have made in your analysis.

CHESTER CARPET LIMITED

Working paper for the financial appraisal of a new machine

for the production department

DISCOUNTED CASH FLOW

Year	Cash Flow	Discount Factor at 10%	Discounted Cash Flow
	£		£
2004	_____	1.000	_____
2005	_____	0.909	_____
2006	_____	0.826	_____
2007	_____	0.751	_____
2008	_____	0.683	_____
Net Present Value (NPV)			━━━━━━

PAYBACK PERIOD

Year	Cash Flow	Cumulative Cash Flow
	£	£
2004	_____	_____
2005	_____	_____
2006	_____	_____
2007	_____	_____
2008	_____	_____

Payback period = _____

9.4 Towan Kitchens Limited makes 'flat-pack' kitchens which are sold to the public in DIY stores. You are an accounts assistant and have just received the following memorandum from the General Manager:

MEMORANDUM

To: Accounts Assistant

From: General Manager

Date: 15 September 2004

Manufacture of kitchen worktops

As you know, the manufacture of worktops is currently contracted out to another company at a cost to us of £200,000 per year. The production manager has proposed that we should buy the special equipment needed to do the work ourselves in-house, thus making savings on the costs of the contract work. The equipment will cost £300,000 and we will also have to pay the following costs over the next five years:

	operators' wages £	repairs and maintenance £	other costs £
2005	42,000	8,000	33,000
2006	64,000	12,000	37,000
2007	68,000	22,000	42,000
2008	68,000	25,000	44,000
2009	70,000	30,000	45,000

If we go ahead, the equipment will be bought at the end of this year ready for production to start in 2005. At the end of 2009 the equipment will have a scrap value of £10,000.

Please appraise this proposal from a financial viewpoint. I need to know the payback period and the net present value. As you know, the maximum required payback period is three years and, for net present value, we require a return of 14%.

Task 1

Use the working paper on the next page to calculate the net present value and the payback period of the proposed investment. Ignore inflation and calculate all money amounts to the nearest £.

Task 2

Write a report, dated 18 September 2004, to the General Manager evaluating the proposal from a financial viewpoint. State any assumptions you have made in your analysis.

TOWAN KITCHENS LIMITED

Working paper for the financial appraisal of in-house worktop manufacture

CASH FLOWS

Year	Savings £	Total Costs £	Cash Flow £
2004	–		
2005			
2006			
2007			
2008			
2009			

DISCOUNTED CASH FLOW

Year	Cash Flow £	Discount Factor at 14%	Discounted Cash Flow £
2004		1.000	
2005		0.877	
2006		0.769	
2007		0.675	
2008		0.592	
2009		0.519	

Net Present Value (NPV)

PAYBACK PERIOD

Year	Cash Flow £	Cumulative Cash Flow £
2004		
2005		
2006		
2007		
2008		
2009		

Payback period =

9.5   The research department of Zelah Chemical Company has discovered a wonder drug which cures the symptoms of the common cold within a matter of hours. The company has decided to develop the new drug – to be called 'Zelahcold' – and the Managing Director has asked you, the accounts assistant, to appraise the financial effects of this project.

For all new projects the company requires an annual rate of return of 10 per cent for net present value, and a maximum payback period of three years in terms of revenue.

You are given the following information relating to this project.

	Year 0 £000	Year 1 £000	Year 2 £000	Year 3 £000	Year 4 £000	Year 5 £000
Development costs	–	110	–	–	–	–
Sales revenue	–	–	55	90	120	120
Variable costs	–	–	30	30	40	35
10% Present value factor	1.000	0.909	0.826	0.751	0.683	0.621

Task 1

Calculate for the new project:

(a)   the payback period

(b)   the net present value

Task 2

Use the data from Task 1 to prepare a report to the Managing Director on the new product. Your report should:

(a)   identify *two* additional items of information relevant to appraising this project

(b)   make a recommendation to accept or reject the project

10 REPORTING INFORMATION

10.1 Consider the following situations:

Case 1: the manager of a telephone call centre dealing with insurance claims is considering the number of lines and the number of staff needed to answer calls in the coming year.

Case 2: Andrew Miller is a sole trader running his own plumbing business. He currently works long hours to complete all the available work and is considering whether to expand the business by taking on trainees or qualified employees.

For each of the cases 1 and 2, give two examples of:

(a) external information that would be useful

(b) internal financial information that would be useful

(c) internal non-financial information that would be useful

10.2 In the diagram below there are six categories of data. For each of the following types of data, enter the corresponding number into the box on the diagram for the appropriate category.

1 the number of employees on the payroll this month

2 total sales revenue figures for the last three years

3 current wage rates for employees

4 the expected number of orders from customers in the next year

5 the number of labour hours available this week

6 the number of product units sold last year

7 the forecast cost of a raw material for the next year

8 the difference between the target profit and the actual profit for last year

9 the number of machine hours available for the next six months

10 the total hours of production labour used last year

11 the current cost per unit of raw materials

12 the expected market price of a product in the next year

13 the current time taken to carry out a specific task

14 the total production cost per unit of a product last year

15 the target profits for each division of a company for next year

	FINANCIAL	NON-FINANCIAL
PAST		
PRESENT		
FUTURE		

10.3 (a) Explain the difference between flat and hierarchical organisation structures.

(b) For any organisation(s) with which you are familiar, consider whether the structure tends to be flat or hierarchical.

(c) For each of the cases 1 to 6 below, consider whether the organisation structure could be described as flat or hierarchical.

Case

1 a taxi service with 15 taxi drivers and a manager in the central office

2 a college that has a principal, vice principals, managers of human resources, finance, the library, quality assurance and the teaching departments, and leaders of staff teams within departments

3 a police force with national, regional and district managers

4 a private college running accountancy training courses, which is run by an executive director and employs a number of lecturers

5 a telephone call centre with a manager and 35 telephone operators

6 a manufacturing business run by a board of directors to whom divisional managers report, each division being split into departments with a general manager and a production supervisor for each department

10.4 Suggest items of data that are likely to be included in:

• a sales report for the manager of a shop

• a sales report for the manager of a chain of shops

10.5 Suggest the types of internal information that are likely to be useful in performance reports for the following organisations:

• a library

• a chain of nightclubs

• a college

• a taxi service

• a chain of clothes shops

10.6 (a) List and explain briefly four features that are necessary for a report to give good quality information.

(b) Explain briefly, giving an example, how the level of responsibility of the person for whom a report is being prepared affects the type of reporting required.

(c) Explain briefly, giving an example, why it is important that information from different sources should be reconciled.

10.7 Working individually or in groups, obtain examples of external information from published material or the internet. For each example, discuss the good and bad features of the presentation of the information and summarise the main points clearly and concisely.

10.8 An important step in the preparation of a report is to look at the data available and identify any obvious features in it, before doing any calculations. Comments on these features may provide material for part of the report.

Without carrying out any calculations, consider the following examples of financial and non-financial information and write brief notes on any aspects of the figures that you notice (such as trends, similarities and differences).

EXAMPLE 1: FOX PLC

Fox plc is a manufacturer of sports equipment and has 3 production departments, A, B and C.

Fox plc Production for the first quarter of the year

Production Department:	A	B	C
Number of units of output	70,000	35,000	77,000
Total production wages	£150,000	£90,000	£150,000

EXAMPLE 2: DEER LIMITED

Deer Ltd owns a chain of shops selling baby clothes and equipment and collects together data for the shops in four regions.

Deer Ltd Sales Revenue for November by region

Region	North	South	East	West
Total sales	£275,000	£400,000	£190,000	£220,000
Number of shops	10	14	8	8

EXAMPLE 3: DART LIMITED AND EDEN LIMITED

Dart Ltd and Eden Ltd are two companies within the same industry.

Profits for five years

Year	1	2	3	4	5
Profit (£000s):					
Dart Ltd	560	590	610	650	680
Eden Ltd	760	770	800	780	760

EXAMPLE 4: WEBB DELIVeries

Webb Deliveries is a parcel delivery service based in a medium sized town.

Webb Deliveries Quarterly Data: January to March

	January	February	March
Number of vans	4	4	6
Miles travelled	12,400	13,000	22,000

EXAMPLE 5: RED LIMITED

Red Ltd is a manufacturer of disposable paper cups for vending machines.

Red Ltd monthly usage of raw materials April to June

	April	May	June
Units of raw material used	45,000	42,000	38,000
Cost of raw material used	£360,000	£360,000	£380,000

10.9 For each of the examples 1 to 5 given in 10.8 above, suggest one further type of data that you consider would add to the usefulness of the information.

10.10 Working individually or in a group, using the business press or the websites of individual organisations and business analysts, collect examples of performance reports for various organisations. For each example, identify the main points covered in the report and look carefully at any numerical information and graphs or charts. Consider the following questions:

- can you see immediately what the report is about?

- does the report communicate the information clearly?

- is there any attempt to mislead the reader of the report?

- do any tables or diagrams help the reader to understand the information?

- does the report provide useful information for the intended users?

11 MEASURING PERFORMANCE

11.1 Walton plc: Departmental monthly wages

Walton plc has five departments, A, B, C, D and E. The monthly wages for each of the departments are as follows:

A	B	C	D	E	Total
£24,500	£30,625	£15,925	£36,750	£14,700	£122,500

You are to:

(a)   Calculate, for each department, the monthly cost of wages as a percentage of the total monthly wages of Walton plc.

(b)   Calculate the new monthly wages for each department and the total for the company if departments A, B and C are given a 4% wage increase and departments D and E are given a 2% wage increase.

(c)   Calculate the percentage increase in the total monthly wages for Walton plc that would result from the wage increases described in part (b).

11.2 Clover Cars have several branches and a total of 10 people selling cars. The following data relates to the weekly sales of cars over a 12-week period.

Clover Cars weekly sales

Week	1	2	3	4	5	6
Number of cars sold	20	18	20	24	25	28

Week	7	8	9	10	11	12
Number of cars sold	30	30	26	22	20	22

The expected average number of cars to be sold is 30 per week.

You are to calculate:

(a)   the weekly labour productivity (output per employee)

(b)   the weekly efficiency percentage (to the nearest %)

(c)   the labour productivity and the efficiency percentage for the whole twelve-week period.

Set out your calculations on a spreadsheet or table. Comment briefly on the results and identify one way in which the reporting of sales data for Clover Cars could be improved.

11.3   Lite Luggage Limited is a manufacturer of luggage for air travel. The company sells its product to wholesalers. During the year it records the following figures for units made and sold and total production cost of units made and sold.

Lite Luggage Limited monthly production

	Units made and sold (thousands)	Production costs (£000s)
January	40	740
February	35	728
March	30	720
April	40	760
May	32	704
June	36	720
July	40	780
August	35	735
September	32	720
October	30	690
November	36	738
December	40	760

You are to calculate:

(a)   the production cost per unit in each month (to the nearest penny)

(b)   the total units made and sold, total production cost and cost per unit for the first six months, January to June

(c)   the total units made and sold, total production cost and cost per unit for the second six months, July to December

Set out the data and your answers on a spreadsheet or in a table and comment briefly on the results.

11.4   This activity uses some of the data and answers relating to Lite Luggage Limited from 11.3 above, together with additional information given below.

Lite Luggage Limited sells its product at £28 per unit in the first half of the year and £30 per unit in the second half of the year.

The overheads and capital employed during the year are as shown in the table.

You are to complete the table below or continue with your spreadsheet from 11.3 and:

(a)   use your answers to 11.3, parts (b) and (c), to calculate the Sales Revenue for the six months January to June and the six months July to December

(b)   enter the total production cost of units made and sold for each six-month period

(c)   calculate the gross profit and the net profit for each six-month period as shown in the table below

(d)   calculate the gross profit percentage and the net profit percentage for each six-month period (to the nearest %)

(e)   calculate the capital productivity and return on capital employed for each six-month period

(f)   complete the 'total for year' column as shown on the table below

(g)   comment briefly on the results of your calculations.

Lite Luggage Limited	January-June	July-December	Total for year
Units made and sold (000s)			
Selling price	£28 per unit	£30 per unit	
	£000s	£000s	£000s
Sales Revenue			
Production cost of units made and sold			
Gross Profit			
Overheads	600	620	1,220
Net Profit			
Gross Profit %			
Net Profit %			
Capital Employed (£000s)	3,500	3,500	3,500
Capital productivity (sales revenue per £1 of capital employed)			
Return on Capital Employed			

11.5   Daisy's Direct is a mail order gift service and has 4 employees working in the packing department. These employees normally work 38 hours per week. During a period of 8 weeks, the following hours were recorded by the 4 employees.

Daisy's Direct Packing Department: weekly hours								
Week:	1	2	3	4	5	6	7	8
Employee	Hours per week							
P Leigh	36	42	36	30	32	30	36	38
A Patel	36	40	35	36	32	32	38	38
R Napier	36	41	35	35	32	30	36	38
D Davis	36	43	36	38	30	32	36	38

You are to:

(a)   calculate the total hours worked in each week and the total hours worked by each employee in the 8-week period.

(b)   calculate the labour utilisation percentage for each week and for the whole 8-week period (to the nearest %)

(c)   comment briefly on the results.

11.6   The following figures were recorded by Unicreme Ice Cream Ltd for the four quarters of Year 2.

Production figures for Unicreme Ice Cream Ltd: Year 2				
Quarter	1	2	3	4
Units produced and sold	30,000	96,000	120,000	48,000
Expected output (units)	22,000	88,000	124,000	42,000
Sales (£)	60,000	175,000	215,000	95,000
Cost of production (£)	41,000	81,600	96,000	50,000
Hours worked	500	1,000	1,200	600

You are to calculate for each quarter:

(a)   labour productivity (sales (£) per hour worked)

(b)   units produced per hour worked

(c)   efficiency percentage

(d)   cost of production per unit

11.7 This activity uses some of the same data relating to Unicreme Ice Cream Ltd as in activity 11.6 above. The data required is repeated in the table below, together with additional figures for quarterly overheads.

Production figures for Unicreme Ice Cream Ltd: Year 2

Quarter	1	2	3	4	Total
	£	£	£	£	
Sales	60,000	175,000	215,000	95,000	
Cost of production	41,000	81,600	96,000	50,000	
Gross Profit					
Overheads	30,000	50,000	50,000	30,000	160,000
Net profit/(loss)					
Gross profit margin					
Net profit margin					

You are to:

(a) fill in the blank rows and columns in the table either manually or using a spreadsheet

(b) given that the capital employed by Unicreme in year 2 was £400,000, calculate for Year 2:

   (i) the capital productivity (sales per £1 of capital employed)

   (ii) the Return on Capital Employed

11.8 Davis Limited manufactures a fibre-glass product that requires the material to be cut and moulded before the product is finished and packed. The following budgeted and actual data relates to the four departments of Davis Ltd for a given year.

Davis Ltd Production and Labour Data for the year

Department	Cutting	Moulding	Finishing	Packing
Budgeted output (units)	200,000	200,000	180,000	180,000
Labour hours available	20,000	25,000	24,000	12,000
Actual output (units)	198,000	195,000	175,000	175,000
Actual labour hours worked	19,600	24,500	23,500	12,000
Actual cost of labour (£)	138,600	156,000	157,500	70,000
Average number of employees	11	14	13	7

You are to:

Set up the data on a spreadsheet or table and calculate the following performance indicators for each department of Davis Ltd:

(a)   labour productivity as actual units of output per employee

(b)   efficiency percentage comparing actual output with budgeted output

(c)   labour utilisation percentage comparing actual hours with available hours

(d)   actual cost of labour per unit of actual output

(e)   for one of the performance indicators calculated, suggest a reason why comparison between the departments of Davis Ltd may be unfair to the employees.

11.9   You are an accounting technician employed by Mixed Retailers plc, which owns a large number of stores selling a wide variety of products throughout the UK. Mixed Retailers plc is currently investigating the performance of a number of companies retailing electrical goods with a view to purchasing a chain of stores in that sector of the market.

As an accounting technician in the accounting department of Mixed Retailers plc you have been asked by the chief accountant to carry out a number of analyses of the accounts of two companies retailing electrical goods.

You are to:

(a)   Look at the following data for two years for two companies – Alpha and Beta – see the next page.

Analyse the data by completing the table on the next page.

Show the average size of store and sales per employee to the nearest whole number.

Show net profit/sales as a percentage to two decimal places.

(b)   Prepare a report for the chief accountant comparing the performance of Alpha and Beta.

Your report should be well-presented and address the following issues:

• size

• profitability

• efficiency

Your report should conclude by presenting the key differences in performance between the two companies. You should not attempt to make recommendations.

PERFORMANCE DATA

	Company Alpha		Company Beta	
Year	2003	2004	2003	2004
Number of stores	281	279	226	231
Total area (sq m)	1,110,000	1,200,000	191,000	180,000
Number of employees	14,700	16,200	5,050	5,100
Sales (£m)	1,050	1,350	495	510
Net profit (£m)	51.1	52.0	15.7	16.8
Sales per sq m (£)	946	1,125	2,592	2,833
Average size of store (sq m)				
Net profit/sales (%)				
Sales per employee (£)				

11.10 You are an accounting technician working for City Hotels Limited, which owns three hotels in London.

- The Station Hotel is situated near a main railway station and its customers are mainly railway travellers, business people and weekend visitors.

- The Airport Hotel is situated near the airport and its customers are virtually all air travellers who stay in the hotel either before or after their flight.

- The Central Hotel is situated in the city centre and is used mainly by tourists, business people and weekend visitors.

City Hotels Limited wishes to compare the performances of the three hotels and has asked you to carry out a series of analyses to enable this to be done.

Basic Data

	Station Hotel	Airport Hotel	Central Hotel
Number of Rooms	140	210	90
Standard Room Tariff	£84.00	£90.00	£120.00

Notes:

- Each hotel has only double rooms. The standard room tariff is the price of a double room per night.
- City Hotels Limited runs a variety of discount schemes and special offers whereby rooms can be obtained at cheaper rates.

City Hotels Limited

Performance Statistics for the week ended 31 May 2004

	Sun	Mon	Tues	Wed	Thurs	Fri	Sat
Station Hotel:							
No. of Rooms Let	80	110	108	106	105	96	121
Total Room Revenue	£5,712	£8,632	£8,624	£8,648	£8,442	£7,228	£6,920
Room Occupancy Rate	57%	79%	77%	76%	75%	69%	86%
Average Rate per Room Let	£71.40	£78.47	£79.85	£81.58	£80.40	£75.29	£57.19
Airport Hotel:							
No. of Rooms Let	182	192	186	174	195	184	173
Total Room Revenue	£16,148	£16,920	£16,482	£15,084	£16,836	£15,680	£15,036
Room Occupancy Rate	87%	91%	89%	83%	93%	88%	82%
Average Rate per Room Let	£88.73	£88.13	£88.61	£86.69	£86.34	£85.22	£86.91
Central Hotel:							
No. of Rooms Let	64	68	69	46	52	65	82
Total Room Revenue	£6,880	£7,304	£7,082	£4,832	£5,734	£6,432	£7,924
Room Occupancy Rate	71%	76%	77%	51%	58%	72%	91%
Average Rate per Room Let	£107.50	£107.41	£102.64	£105.04	£110.27	£98.95	£96.63

You are to:

(a)   Complete the Summary Performance Statistics (see the next page) for City Hotels Limited.

City Hotels Limited

Summary Performance Statistics for the week ended 31 May 2004

	Station Hotel	Airport Hotel	Central Hotel
Total Rooms Let			
Average Room Occupancy Rate			
Total Room Revenue			
Average Rate per Room Let			

Note: Average room occupancy rate is to be shown to the nearest whole percentage. The average rate per room let is to be shown to the nearest penny.

(b)   Prepare a report for City Hotels Limited, comparing the performances of the three hotels for the week ending 31 May 2004. Use the information given, together with the statistics prepared by you in part (a).

Your report should address the following issues:

• room occupancy rates

• rates per room let

• possible recommendations for the future, giving evidence for your reasoning

• any limitations in the data provided

12 CHARTS, AVERAGES AND INDICES

12.1 Kaye Limited

You work for Kaye Limited, a company which has branches in three regions: North, Midlands and South. You have collected together sales revenue figures for the first six months of the year, January to June, for each of the company's three regions. The figures are given in thousands of pounds and are as follows (in date order):

North: 270, 310, 330, 320, 300, 290

Midlands: 350, 360, 375, 375, 380, 385

South: 180, 185, 200, 220, 240, 250

You are to:

Set out the above data in a table or on a spreadsheet, including totals for each month and totals for each region for the 6 months January to June.

12.2 Kaye Limited

Using the table or spreadsheet of data prepared in activity 12.1, construct the following diagrams to illustrate Kaye Limited's regional figures. For each diagram, comment briefly on what it does and does not show.

(a)   line graph

(b)   compound bar chart

(c)   component bar chart

(d)   percentage component bar chart

(e)   pie chart, using the six-monthly totals only

You may construct the diagrams either manually or using a computer.

12.3   Clover Cars have several branches and a total of 10 people selling cars. The following data relates to the sales made by each of the 10 people over a 12-week period.

	Clover Cars Sales Analysis									
Sales person:	A	B	C	D	E	F	G	H	I	J
Number of cars sold:	18	31	24	28	22	31	35	38	31	27
Sales value of cars sold (£000s)	350	310	250	260	390	300	390	440	390	350

You are to:

(a)   Calculate the total number of cars sold in the period

(b)   Calculate the total sales value of cars sold in the period

(c)   Using your answers to (a) and (b), calculate:

    (i)   the mean number of cars sold per sales person

    (ii)   the mean value of cars sold per sales person

    (iii)   the mean value per car of all the cars sold in the period

(d)   Sort each set of data into size order and hence identify the median and the mode of each set.

(e)   Construct a simple bar chart to show the value of the cars sold by each of the sales staff.

You may carry out the activities either manually or using a computer.

12.4   Monthly Sales Revenue figures (in £000s) are shown below for the South region of Kaye Limited for a given year.

Kaye Ltd South Region monthly sales (£000s)			
January	180	July	256
February	185	August	268
March	200	September	280
April	220	October	285
May	240	November	306
June	250	December	313

You are to:

(a)   Construct a table showing the monthly sales revenue in a single column and calculate a 3-point moving average trend.

(b)   Calculate the average monthly increment in the trend (to the nearest whole number in £000s)

(c)   Use your answer to (b) to forecast the trend in monthly sales revenue for January and February of the next year

(d)   Construct a graph showing the original data and your forecasts of the trend for January and February of the next year.

12.5 Unicreme Ice Cream Limited has recorded the following quarterly sales volumes over the last three years.

Unicreme Ice Cream Ltd: Sales volume in thousands of packs				
Quarter	1	2	3	4
Year 1	14	80	116	34
Year 2	30	96	120	48
Year 3	32	100	132	48

You are to:

(a) Set up a table to work out four-point moving averages on these figures

(b) Calculate centred averages to obtain trend figures and seasonal variations, working to the nearest whole number

(c) Calculate the average quarterly increment in the trend to the nearest whole number

(d) Use your answer to (c) to forecast the trend for the four quarters of Year 4, assuming it continues to increase at the same rate

(e) (Optional) Calculate the average seasonal variations to the nearest whole number and use them to forecast the sales volumes for the four quarters of Year 4

(f) Plot the original data, the trend line and your forecasts on a graph for Years 1 to 4.

12.6 Lockwood plc employs 400 people. The employees' gross weekly wages (to the nearest £) are as follows:

Lockwood plc: analysis of gross weekly wages

Gross weekly wages £	Number of employees
0 to 300	40
301 to 400	50
401 to 500	150
501 to 600	100
601 to 700	50
701 to 1,100	10
	400

You are to:

(a)   Calculate the cumulative frequency of the data

(b)   Draw up a cumulative frequency graph

(c)   Identify from your graph the median gross weekly wages for the employees of Lockwood plc.

12.7   The comparative monthly sales figures for this year and last year for the North region of Kaye Limited are shown below.

Kaye Ltd North Region Sales

	Last year	This year
	£000s	£000s
January	250	270
February	260	310
March	280	330
April	290	320
May	290	300
June	280	290
July	270	280
August	270	270
September	260	260
October	270	280
November	270	290
December	280	300

You are to:

(a)   Draw up a table with the two columns given and two additional columns showing the cumulative sales for this year and the moving annual total sales

(b)   Check that the December cumulative sales figure and the final annual moving total both agree with the total sales for this year

(c)   Draw up a Z chart using the data from your table.

12.8 The following table shows the sales and net profit figures for Broom Estate Agents for the last five years, together with the Retail Prices Index for those years.

Broom Estate Agents: sales and net profit for years 1 to 5		
Sales	*Net Profit*	*RPI*
£000s	*£000s*	
Year 1	800	120	155
Year 2	890	130	163
Year 3	920	140	169
Year 4	950	150	176
Year 5	990	160	189

You are to:

(a) Convert the sales and net profit figures into index numbers, using year 1 as a base

(b) Adjust the sales and net profit figures for the changing price levels shown by the Retail Prices Index. Put the figures into year 5 terms and give your answers to the nearest whole number.

(c) Comment briefly on the trends shown in your answers to (a) and (b) above.

12.9 You are an accounting technician employed by Mixed Retailers plc, which owns a large number of stores selling a wide variety of products throughout the UK. Mixed Retailers plc is currently investigating the performance of a number of companies retailing electrical goods with a view to purchasing a chain of stores in that sector of the market.

Mixed Retailers plc is thinking of purchasing Company Gamma. The chief accountant of Mixed Retailers plc is concerned about some comments made in the annual report of Gamma. In this report the managing director of Gamma makes the following statement:

'Although sales have increased each year from 2000 to 2004, operating profits took a slight dip in 2002 and 2003 before rising to record levels in 2004.'

Relevant figures from the report are as follows:

	2000	2001	2002	2003	2004
Sales (£m)	3003.6	3235.4	3288.8	3547.9	4479.4
Operating profit (£m)	237.6	240.5	218.9	208.7	318.2
% Change in Operating Profit	–	1.22%	- 8.98%	- 4.66%	52.47%
Operating profit as % of sales	7.91%	7.43%	6.66%	5.88%	7.10%
Sales at 2004 prices (£m)					
Operating profit at 2004 prices (£m)	269.5	264.1	231.1	214.2	318.2
Trade Price Index	133.3	137.7	143.2	147.3	151.2

You are to:

(a) Complete the table above by calculating sales for each year at 2004 prices using the Trade Price Index. Your figures should be shown as £m rounded to one decimal place.

(b) Prepare a line graph, showing the trend in sales and operating profit at 2004 prices from 2000 to 2004.

(c) Write a memo, stating whether you agree or disagree with the statement made by the managing director of Gamma. Support your conclusions with evidence, using the data given and your answers to (a) and (b).

12.10 You are an accounting technician working for City Hotels Limited, which owns three hotels in London.

- The Station Hotel is situated near a main railway station and its customers are mainly railway travellers, business people and weekend visitors.

- The Airport Hotel is situated near the airport and its customers are virtually all air travellers who stay in the hotel either before or after their flight.

- The Central Hotel is situated in the city centre and is used mainly by tourists, business people and weekend visitors.

City Hotels Limited wishes to compare the performances of the three hotels and has asked you to compare the revenue from rooms let for the three hotels over the last five years.

City Hotels Limited

Revenue from Rooms Let 1999 - 2003

	1999	2000	2001	2002	2003
Station Hotel	£2,300,000	£2,500,000	£2,400,000	£2,500,000	£2,600,000
Airport Hotel	£2,500,000	£2,800,000	£4,600,000	£5,200,000	£5,500,000
Central Hotel	£1,700,000	£1,800,000	£1,700,000	£1,900,000	£2,200,000

You are to:

(a) Prepare a clearly labelled line graph showing the performance of the three hotels for the period 1999-2003.

(b) Prepare a memorandum for the hotel accountant. The memorandum should:

- analyse the trends revealed by the graph prepared in part (a)

- highlight any limitations in trends revealed by your analysis

13 REPORT WRITING

A note on further opportunities for report writing

In addition to the Activities relating to Chapter 13 presented here, you are required to write reports for Activities 9.1, 9.3 (Task 2), 9.4 (Task 2) and 9.5 (Task 2).

In the chapter activities for chapters 10, 11 and 12 you will find a variety of case studies that can be used for report writing practice. In particular, activities 11.2 to 11.5 ask for comments on the results. The comments may be put into report format. In addition, Activities 11.9, 11.10, 12.9 and 12.10 include memos and reports.

In all these cases look back at your answers and review them to ensure that they are in a suitable format and that they are clear, concise, objective, accurate and do not include jargon or slang.

The activities for Chapter 14 and subsequent simulations and practice exams also include writing reports for further practice.

13.1 BCL Ltd specialises in the manufacture of computer hardware and software and the provision of computer consultancy services. In recent years, the software and consultancy business has expanded.

BCL Ltd sells hardware to both commercial and government organisations. The commercial hardware market is becoming more competitive and development costs are rising. The government hardware business is currently restricted by government spending limits, but is expected to improve in the long term. Government hardware contracts often provide additional work for the software and consultancy division of BCL Ltd.

You work in the finance department of BCL Ltd and have been given the following data for the years 2003 and 2004, relating to the three divisions of the company: Commercial Hardware, Government Hardware and Software and Consultancy. The performance figures given in bold type for the year 2004 and a report on the results have been prepared by a trainee.

You are to:

Correct and rewrite (or prepare using a spreadsheet) the table of performance indicators for BCL Ltd for the given years. Rewrite the performance report on these results as an example of good practice for the trainee.

BCL LTD DATA FOR THE YEAR 2004

	Commercial Hardware	Government Hardware	Software and Consultancy
	£000s	£000s	£000s
Sales revenue	15,957	24,768	11,368
Development costs	6,376	7,832	2,134
Other costs	7,215	8,150	3,716
Net profit	2,366	8,786	5,518
Number of employees	831	607	423

BCL LTD PERFORMANCE INDICATORS FOR 2003 AND 2004

	2003	*2004*
Commercial Hardware		
Sales revenue (£000s)	17,643	15,957
Net profit margin	17.5%	**12.1%**
Development costs as a percentage of sales	34.7%	**40.0%**
Sales per employee (£)	22,107	**19,202**
Government Hardware		
Sales revenue (£000s)	25,974	24,768
Net profit margin	36.6%	**35.5%**
Development costs as a percentage of sales	30.9%	**31.6%**
Sales per employee (£)	41,200	**40,408**
Software and Consultancy		
Sales revenue (£000s)	9,276	11,368
Net profit margin	39.4%	**48.5%**
Development costs as a percentage of sales	21.7%	**18.3%**
Sales per employee (£)	23,614	**26,875**

REPORT

To: Senior Accountant

From: Trainee

Date: January 2005

Subject:

Total sales and per employee for Commercial H have both gone down in 2004 and so has net profit % and development costs went up to 40.0%. These results are extremely bad and this division should be closed down straight away.

For Gov Hardware, nothing seems to have changed much. Sales in total and per employee are down and the net profit has decreased from 36.6% to 35.5%. Development costs are about the same. I think they should do more to try and improve their sales and profits.

The performance indicators are all good for the software and consultancy. The net profit went up from 39.4% to 48.5%, much better than the other two divisions. Sales in total and per employee have both increased and the percentage development costs has been cut. They should expand this side of the business.

13.2 Rainbow plc is a paint manufacturer and the information below relates to Rainbow plc for the year ended 30 June 2004.

Rainbow plc

Summary Profit and Loss Account for the year ended 30 June 2004

	£000s	£000s
Sales		3,500
Less: Cost of Sales		
Opening Stock	30	
Cost of Production	1,650	
Less: Closing Stock	(90)	
		1,590
Gross Profit		1,910
Administration	780	
Selling and Distribution	505	
		1,285
Net Profit		625
Capital employed		2,840

You are to:

(a) Calculate the following ratios for Rainbow plc for the given year

Gross profit as a percentage of sales

Net profit as a percentage of sales

Return on Capital Employed (ROCE)

Capital productivity as Sales (£)/Capital employed

(b) Given the following comparative data for Rainbow plc for the year ended 30 June 2003, write a short report giving your comments on the company's performance.

Rainbow plc Performance data for the year ended 30 June 2003

Gross profit as a percentage of sales	52%
Net profit as a percentage of sales	21%
Return on Capital Employed	24%
Capital productivity	£1.16

13.3 The Wichenford Bus Company runs regular bus services on two main routes and the managers of the company wish to compare the profitability of these routes over the last 6-month period. You are given the following information for the two routes for the given period:

Bus services data for 6 months

	Route A	Route B
Number of vehicles used	6	8
Total mileage for 6 months	35,000 miles	47,000 miles
Sales Revenue	£157,500	£169,200
Total costs	£148,000	£156,700

You are to:

(a) Set up the data on a table or spreadsheet and calculate for the given period for each route:
- average sales revenue per mile
- total cost per mile
- average mileage per vehicle
- net profit
- net profit as a percentage of sales revenue
- net profit per mile

(b) Prepare a short report for the management of the Wichenford Bus Company, commenting on the results for routes A and B for the given period. Include in your report a compound bar chart to show how the two routes compare for sales revenue per mile, total cost per mile and net profit per mile.

13.4 Bradshaw plc runs two chains of shops selling electrical goods, under the names Brad and Shaw. The Brad chain of shops offers lower prices but a smaller range of goods than the Shaw chain.

The data below relates to the two chains of shops for the two years ended 30 September 2003 and 2004.

Bradshaw plc Data for the years ended 30 September:

	2003		2004	
	Brad	*Shaw*	*Brad*	*Shaw*
Sales (£000s)	33,000	58,000	36,000	55,000
Net profit (£000s)	6,000	10,000	6,000	11,000
Number of shops	9	14	10	11
Total area in square metres	17,100	39,000	20,000	32,000
Number of employees	630	850	750	680

You are to:

(a) Set up the data on a table or spreadsheet and calculate for each chain for each year:
- the average area in square metres per shop
- the sales revenue per square metre
- the sales revenue per employee
- the net profit as a percentage of sales

(b) Prepare a report for the management of Bradshaw plc comparing the performance of the two chains of shops over the given two year period. Include in your report a component bar chart showing the split of the total number of shops owned by Bradshaw plc into the two chains in each of the two given years. For comparison, include a similar chart using the area in square metres.

13.5 The Coast and Inland Railway Company runs three lines: a commuter line, a coastal line serving holiday resorts and a rural line serving local communities. Some passengers use the rural line to link up with the commuter line. The coastal line carries more passengers in the holiday season. The following data relates to the three lines for the year ended 30 June 2004. The rural line is not profitable and the management of the railway is considering closing this line.

You are to:

(a) Complete the last three rows of the table on the next page, using a spreadsheet if possible.

(b) Prepare a report for the manager of the Coast and Inland Railway Company, giving your comments on the differences between the three lines and on the proposal to close the rural line.

COAST AND INLAND RAILWAY: DATA FOR YEAR ENDED 30 JUNE 2004				
Line:	**Commuter**	**Coastal**	**Rural**	**Total**
Income (£000s)	75,000	43,500	19,500	138,000
Total Costs (£000s)	64,500	39,000	19,800	123,300
Number of passengers (000s)	9,500	6,800	3,600	19,900
Seats available (000s)	10,000	11,300	10,000	31,300
Income per passenger (£)				
Cost per passenger (£)				
Percentage of available seats used				

13.6 You are an accounting technician working for a company that specialises in consultancy to the coal mining industry. Your company has been approached by a small coal mining company that has two mines:

1　　an underground deep mine in the north of the country at Thorington

2　　a surface open-cast mine in the south of the country at Seaforth

The output from the underground coal mine at Thorington is mainly for home consumption, whilst the output from the open-cast coal mine at Seaforth is primarily for export. The home market for coal is under threat from competition from cheaper overseas coal and home produced natural gas, whilst the overseas market is more traditional and there is a steady demand.

The coal mining company wants to develop a third mine and is unsure whether it should be a deep or open-cast mine. The third mine would be in the locality of one of its two existing mines. The coal mining company has carried out the prospecting and exploration stages near to the location of its current mines and is now ready to proceed to the development and exploitation stages at the chosen site. Work to date has shown that yields and costs for both potential mines would be similar to the yields and costs of the existing mines in the locality .

The data on the next page relates to the performance of the Thorington underground mine and the Seaforth open-cast surface mine over the last three years.

	2003	2004	2005
Tonnes of coal excavated (000s)			
Thorington	471.6	472.2	472.9
Seaforth	293.6	315.2	341.7
Number of employees			
Thorington	237	244	253
Seaforth	162	164	170
Excavation costs (£000s)			
Thorington	13,456	13,892	13,999
Seaforth	9,117	9,135	9,189
Net profit (£000s)			
Thorington	6,943	6,995	7,083
Seaforth	4,437	4,839	5,173

(a) You are given the following table of performance statistics. Complete the table for the Seaforth coal mine on the next page.

PERFORMANCE STATISTICS

THORINGTON UNDERGROUND DEEP MINE 2003-2005

	2003	2004	2005
Coal extracted per employee (tonnes)	1,990	1,935	1,869
Excavation costs per tonne of coal excavated (£)	28.53	29.42	29.60
Net profit per tonne of coal excavated (£)	14.72	14.81	14.98
Net profit per employee (£000)	29.30	28.67	28.00

SEAFORTH OPEN-CAST MINE 2003-2005

	2003	2004	2005
Coal extracted per employee (tonnes)			
Excavation costs per tonne of coal excavated (£)			
Net profit per tonne of coal excavated (£)			
Net profit per employee (£000)			

Note: show figures to the same number of decimal places as for the Thorington mine.

(b) The finance director has asked you to review the coal excavated per employee at the Thorington and Seaforth mines against the industry average for 2003 to 2005.

	Coal excavated per employee Industry Average (tonnes)
2003	1,890
2004	1,920
2005	1,940

Prepare a clearly labelled line graph showing the performance of the Thorington and Seaforth mines against the industry performance for the period 2003 to 2005.

(c) Prepare a report for your finance director comparing the performance of the Thorington and Seaforth mines. Your report should address the following issues using your results from (a) and (b) and the information available given above:

- profitability
- efficiency
- future outlook

You should advise your finance director which potential mine should be taken forward to the development and exploitation stages by the mining company on the basis of the data available for the two present mines.

14 CONSOLIDATING AND REPORTING INFORMATION

14.1 Sam runs a restaurant and a separate catering service for functions. The data given below relates to the 3 months April to June 2004, together with comparative data for the same period in 2003. Sam has asked you to consolidate the figures for the two parts of the business and report back with your comments, but he asked why you wanted the data for April to June 2003, rather than just comparing April to June 2004 with the previous quarter, January to March 2004.

Sam's Restaurant and Catering Services April-June 2004			
	Restaurant	Catering Services	Total
	£	£	£
Sales	145,000	95,000	
Cost of Sales	85,000	57,000	
Gross Profit	60,000	38,000	
Overheads	39,000	20,000	
Net Profit	21,000	18,000	
Gross Profit margin			
Net Profit margin			
Percentage increases in sales compared to the same period in 2003:			
Sales increase			

Sam's Restaurant and Catering Services April-June 2003			
	Restaurant	Catering Services	Total
	£	£	£
Sales	130,000	80,000	
Cost of Sales	70,000	50,000	
Gross Profit	60,000	30,000	
Overheads	40,000	15,000	
Net Profit	20,000	15,000	
Gross Profit margin			
Net Profit margin			

You are to:

(a) Set up the data on a spreadsheet and complete the total columns, profit margin percentages and percentage increases in sales using formulas. Alternatively, calculate the required figures and enter them in the tables.

(b) Write a short report to Sam (word processed if possible), explaining briefly the main points shown by the completed tables and giving the answer to Sam's query about the data being used for comparison.

14.2 Elmwood Retailers Limited owns three shops selling fashion accessories. Branches P and Q are of similar size. Branch R is a smaller shop. You are given the following table of data to complete for Elmwood Retailers Ltd. No adjustments are needed to the sales or purchases figures for the transfers of stock between the branches.

Elmwood Retailers Ltd **Summary Profit and Loss Account for the year ended 30 June 2004**				
	Branch P £000s	Branch Q £000s	Branch R £000s	Total £000s
Sales	700	900	300	
Opening stock	70	70	40	
Purchases	440	630	200	
Less: Closing stock	60	120	40	
Cost of goods sold				
Gross profit				
Overheads	160	180	60	
Net profit				
Transfers	(30)	20	10	
Gross profit %				
Net profit %				

You are to:

(a) Complete the table using a spreadsheet if possible.

(b) Prepare a short report for the managers of Elmwood Retailers Ltd, explaining briefly the main points shown by the completed table.

14.3 Greenpark Limited has two large golf equipment shops, Green and Park. The following data relates to the week ended 30 June 2004.

On 29 June 2004, £5,000 of stock was sent from Green to Park, but this was not recorded in the books of Park until 2 July 2004.

GREENPARK LIMITED						
RESULTS FOR THE WEEK ENDED 30 JUNE 2004						
	Green		**Park**		**Total**	
	£000s	£000s	£000s	£000s	£000s	£000s
Sales		85		60		
Opening stock	10		9			
Purchases	40		35			
Less: Closing stock	10		15			
Cost of goods sold						
Gross profit						
Overheads		30		20		
Net profit						
Transfers		(5)				
Gross profit %						
Net profit %						

You are to:

(a) Complete the table, using a spreadsheet if possible. Make the appropriate adjustment for stock in transit. (No adjustment need be made to sales or purchases figures.)

(b) Write a memo to the managing director of Greenpark Ltd, commenting briefly on the results for the week ended 30 June 2004.

14.4 Gordon Ltd owns three furniture shops, G1, G2 and G3. The data below relates to Gordon Ltd for the week ending 24 April 2004. In the furniture trade, a sale to an individual customer may sometimes have a high value.

Furniture that cost £1,000 was transferred from G2 during this week, but was not received by G3 until 28 April 2004.

GORDON LTD RESULTS FOR THE WEEK ENDED 24 APRIL 2004				
	G1 £	G2 £	G3 £	Total £
Sales	30,000	16,000	18,000	64,000
Purchases	18,000	10,000	8,000	36,000
Wages	5,000	2,500	3,000	10,500
Other Overheads	7,000	3,500	4,500	15,000
Opening stock	6,000	4,000	5,000	15,000
Closing stock	10,000	5,500	4,000	19,500
Transfers	1,500	(2,500)	–	

You are to:

(a)   Prepare a summary profit and loss account for the week ended 24 April 2004, showing the results for each of the branches and in total. Make the appropriate adjustment for stock in transit. (No adjustment need be made to sales or purchases figures.) Calculate the gross profit percentage and the net profit percentage for each branch and for the company as a whole.

(b)   Write a Memo to the managers of Gordon Ltd, making brief comments on the results for the given week.

14.5 Raymond Retail Ltd runs two shoe shops, one in Eastfield and the other in Westvale. The figures given below relate to the two shops for the year ended 31 December 2003. They include net transfers of stock at cost price between the two shops. When the consolidated profit and loss account is prepared, these transfers will not be included in the sales or purchases.

The records from the Westvale shop show that £15,000 of stock was sent to the Eastfield shop on 27 December 2003. This stock was not recorded in the Eastfield records until 5 January 2004.

RAYMOND RETAIL LTD

BRANCH PROFIT AND LOSS ACCOUNTS FOR THE YEAR ENDED 31 DECEMBER 2003

	Eastfield		Westvale	
	£000s	£000s	£000s	£000s
Sales		360		420
Transfers to Eastfield at cost		–		90
		360		510
Opening stock	80		100	
Purchases	180		290	
Transfers from Westvale at cost	75		–	
Less closing stock	90		80	
Cost of goods sold		245		310
Gross Profit		115		200
Overheads		50		120
Net Profit		65		80

You are to:

(a) Consolidate the figures from the two shops into a profit and loss account for the business for the year ended 31 December 2003, making the necessary adjustments for transfers of stock and stock in transit.

(b) Using the consolidated figures, calculate the gross profit percentage and the net profit percentage for Raymond Retail Ltd for the year ended 31 December 2003.

14.6 This activity continues from 14.5 above, relating to the Eastfield and Westvale stores owned by Raymond Retail Ltd. You are an assistant in the company's accounts office.

The figures given below relate to the two shops for the year ended 31 December 2004. They include net transfers of stock at cost price between the two shops. When the consolidated profit and loss account is prepared, these transfers will not be included in the sales or purchases.

The records from the Eastfield shop show that £10,000 of stock was sent to the Westvale shop on 29 December 2004. This stock was not recorded in the Westvale records until 3 January 2005.

RAYMOND RETAIL LTD

BRANCH PROFIT AND LOSS ACCOUNTS FOR THE YEAR ENDED 31 DECEMBER 2004

	Eastfield		Westvale	
	£000s	£000s	£000s	£000s
Sales		340		550
Transfers to Westvale at cost		50		–
		390		550
Opening stock	90		95	
Purchases	220		295	
Transfers from Eastfield at cost	-		40	
Less closing stock	45		80	
Cost of goods sold		265		350
Gross Profit		125		200
Overheads		75		100
Net Profit		50		100

You are to:

(a) Consolidate the figures from the two shops into a profit and loss account for the business for the year ended 31 December 2004, making the necessary adjustments for transfers of stock and stock in transit.

(b) Using the consolidated figures, calculate the gross profit percentage and the net profit percentage for Raymond Retail Ltd for the year ended 31 December 2004.

(c) Prepare a report for the general manager of Raymond Retail Ltd, collecting together relevant data from this activity and 14.5 above. Your report should comment on the performance of the company and the main differences between the two shops over the two years and be illustrated by one or more appropriate graphs or charts.

14.7 Unicreme Ice Cream Ltd supplies retailers with ice cream through its Sales Division, but the Manufacturing Division also sells direct to customers from the company's kiosks and vans. The quarterly divisional sales figures for year 2 are shown below, together with the company's total sales figures for the four quarters of year 1.

Unicreme Ice Cream Ltd Year 2				
Sales Division		**Manufacturing Division**		
		Direct sales (kiosks and vans)	*Transfers to Sales Division*	*Total*
Quarter	£000s	£000s	£000s	£000s
1	50	10	40	50
2	100	75	80	155
3	115	100	90	190
4	80	15	60	75

Total company sales for Year 1			
Quarter 1 £000s	Quarter 2 £000s	Quarter 3 £000s	Quarter 4 £000s
30	150	200	65

You are to:

(a)   Draw up a table or spreadsheet which shows:

- the consolidated total sales figures for Unicreme Ice Cream Ltd for each quarter of year 2 and for the year

- the comparative total sales figures for year 1

- the cumulative sales figures for each quarter of year 2

- the comparative cumulative total sales figures for each quarter of year 1

- the percentage increase in total annual company sales from year 1 to year 2

(b)   Draw (or derive from the spreadsheet) a graph or chart that you consider to be a useful illustration of the features of the data.

14.8 Dale Hotels Ltd owns a chain of hotels and divides the country into four regions for administrative purposes: South-East, South-West, Midlands and North. The company measures the available capacity of the hotels in terms of the number of guest-days, for example: a hotel with enough space for 100 guests and which is open for 365 days a year would have 100 x 365 = 36,500 guest-days available for the year.

The actual usage of the hotels is measured in customer-days. A comparison of customer-days with the total available guest-days shows how well the hotels have been used during a period.

You are a trainee accountant working in the head office of Dale Hotels Ltd and are given the following data and some tasks to complete. The financial year end for Dale Hotels is 31 December.

Dale Hotels Ltd: Data for the year ended 31 December 2003

Region	South-East	South-West	Midlands	North		Total
Number of hotels	4	4	4	3		
Available guest-days (000s)	140	135	130	100		
Actual customer-days (000s)						
Tourists	45	70	35	50		
Business	60	25	65	25		
Total	105	95	100	75		
Percentage used in 2003	75%	70%	77%	75%		
	£000s	£000s	£000s	£000s		£000s
Sales revenue	5,400	5,600	5,200	4,800		
Total costs	4,590	4,900	4,430	4,150		
Net profit	810	700	770	650		
Average sales revenue per hotel						
Net profit %						
Average sales revenue per customer-day						

Dale Hotels Ltd Sales Revenue for the 4 years 2000-2003			
Year	Total Sales Revenue £000s	Retail Prices Index	Adjusted Total Sales Revenue £000s
2000	19,400	172	
2001	20,300	173	
2002	20,800	178	
2003	21,000	184	

You are to:

(a) Complete both the tables given above. Give the net profit percentages correct to 1 decimal place. In the second table, showing total sales revenue for the 4 years 2000-2003, the Retail Prices Index is to be used to adjust the sales revenue figures to 2003 terms.

(b) Prepare a report for the management of Dale Hotels Ltd including comments on the data in both completed tables. Include in your report a chart to show the split between tourist and business customers in each of the four regions and a line graph to show the total sales revenue for the last four years (before and after adjustment).

15 REPORTS AND RETURNS TO OUTSIDE AGENCIES

15.1 Dale Hotels Ltd is planning to expand its chain of hotels and is seeking a long-term bank loan. An extract from the application form for the loan is given on the next page and you are asked to complete it. (Loan form reproduced by courtesy of AAT).

For completion of the form, you will need to refer to activity 14.8 and the answers for that activity. If you have not yet completed activity 14.8 you will need to do so now, or obtain the answers from your tutor. You will also need the following additional information about Dale Hotels Ltd:

- The net profit calculated in activity 14.8 is after all expenses and before taxation

- The total net profit for Dale Hotels Ltd for the year ended 31 December 2002 was £2,790,000.

- The total gross profit for Dale Hotels Ltd for the year ended 31 December 2003 was £7,875,000.

- The capital employed by Dale Hotels Ltd in the year ended 31 December 2003 was £9,980,000.

LOAN APPLICATION (extract)

Name of applicant company _____

Latest year for which accounting information is available _____

Total sales revenue

In latest year for which accounts are available £ _____

In previous year £ _____

Percentage change (+/-) _____

Net profit after all expenses, before taxation

In latest year for which accounts are available £ _____

In previous year £ _____

Percentage change (+/-) _____

Gross profit margin (%) _____

Net profit margin (%) _____

Return on capital employed (%) _____

Notes

1. In the case of a company with a divisional structure, all figures should refer to the results of the company as a whole, not to individual divisions within the company.

2. Unless otherwise stated, all questions relate to the latest year for which accounting information is available.

3. Figures should be actual historical values, with no indexing for inflation.

4. Return on capital employed is defined as net profit for the year before taxation, divided by total capital employed.

5. Percentages are to be given correct to one decimal place.

15.2 This activity is independent of activities 14.8 and 15.1 above and relates to a single hotel in the Dale Hotels chain – the Skipton Dale Hotel, Devonshire Street, Skipton, North Yorkshire.

Each hotel in the chain is required to submit a quarterly return of statistics to the Regional Tourist Office. You are currently working as assistant manager at the Skipton Dale Hotel and the manager, Beth Lang, has given you some notes about the last quarter, January to March 2004, during which the hotel was open for 90 days.

Notes from hotel manager:

For the 90 days the hotel was open in the quarter January to March 2004, we had 52 rooms available, 45 of them double and the rest single. At that time of year we have more business customers than usual: business customer-days were 3,000 out of a total of 5,250 customer-days for the quarter, the rest being tourists.

You are to complete the Quarterly Return of Statistics, given on the next page, for the Skipton Dale Hotel for the quarter ended 31 March 2004, using the manager's notes and other information given above.

NORTHERN TOURIST AUTHORITY

QUARTERLY RETURN OF STATISTICS

Quarter ended: _____

Name of Hotel: _____

Address:

Manager: _____

Number of rooms:

Double _____ Single _____ Total _____

Number of beds available (2 per double room plus one per single room): _____ (a)

Number of days hotel open this quarter: _____ (b)

Total guest-days available this quarter: (a) x (b) _____ (c)

Customer-days this quarter:

Tourists _____ Business _____ Total _____ (d)

Percentage occupancy: (d) as a percentage of (c) _____

Signed: _____ Date: _____

Job title: _____

15.3 Greenpark Ltd is a company that runs golf equipment shops. (This activity is independent of Activity 14.3. which also features Greenpark Ltd)

Greenpark Ltd financed expansion of one its shops with a long-term loan from the bank. The company undertook to provide trading figures to the bank on a monthly basis, so that the bank may monitor its progress.

A 'Statement of Current Trading Position' is shown on the next page, with some of the figures entered as at 30 June 2004 for Greenpark Ltd.

You are given the following additional information relating to the company's Current Liabilities as at 30 June 2004:

- Greenpark Ltd owes a total of £152,000 to its trade suppliers, most of this having been outstanding for less than 30 days. Only £8,500 of the total has been outstanding for between 31 and 60 days and none has been outstanding for more than 60 days.

- Greenpark Ltd has no overdrawn bank balances. The company owes £1,300 PAYE and £45,600 in VAT. It has no other current liabilities at 30 June 2004.

You are to complete the remaining sections of the Statement of Current Trading Position shown on the next page for Greenpark Ltd as at 30 June 2004.

Statement of Current Trading Position
("Quick Figures")

Business Name	GREENPARK LIMITED
As at (date)	30 JUNE 2004

Current Assets

a. Total Trade Debtors (ie. funds owed to you by your customers) £ 77,700

Please give a breakdown of your trade debtors according to how long they have been outstanding:

Up to 30 days	£	62,100
31 to 60 days	£	14,500
Over 60 days	£	1,100

b. Stock and Work in Progress £ 30,000

c. Cash Held and Total of all Bank and Building Society Credit Balances in your books £ 98,600

d. Other Current Assets (please specify, eg. prepayments) PREPAYMENT: TELEPHONE RENTAL

£ 100

Total Current Assets (a)+(b)+(c)+(d) £ 206,400

Current Liabilities

e. Trade Creditors (ie. funds you owe your suppliers) £

Please give a breakdown of your trade creditors according to how long they have been outstanding:

Up to 30 days	£	
31 to 60 days	£	
Over 60 days	£	

f. Total of all Overdrawn Bank Balances in your books £

g. Pay As You Earn (PAYE) Owed by the Business £

h. Value Added Tax (VAT) Owed by the Business £

i. Other Current Liabilities (please specify, eg. accruals)

£

Total Current Liabilities (e)+(f)+(g)+(h)+(i) £

16 THE PRINCIPLES OF VAT

16.1 Various clients of the firm for which you work, knowing that you are an expert on VAT, ask you about VAT registration. The situations are as follows:

(a) David Backham set up in business exactly 12 months ago, but is not registered for VAT. His sales turnover for the year is £150,000.

(b) Jimmy Blacknap is setting up a limited company this week. He is importing sports cars from Europe and expects his sales for the first month to exceed £200,000.

(c) Alan Cutter is setting up a gardening services business this week and expects his sales for the first month to be approximately £45,000.

(d) Mick Owen is setting up a bookshop this month and expects to sell £150,000 worth of books in the first year of trading. He says that as books are zero-rated, it is hardly worth registering for VAT.

(e) Jenny Barnes is setting up a part-time business selling childrens clothes. She only expects to sell £2,000 of clothes each month. Should she register for VAT?

State what you would reply to these clients, advising them

- whether they have to register

- when they have to register

- any advantages which may result from their registering for VAT

16.2 You are working in the accounts office of a local manufacturing firm. You have been given a batch of invoices to prepare. Among them are five invoices for customers who are quoted a 5% cash discount for settlement within 7 days.

Calculate the VAT due (at the current rate) and the invoice total, using the following table:

invoice	net total (before VAT) £	VAT £	invoice total £
4563	1,265.75		
4567	456.25		
4571	5,678.90		
4575	45.60		
4578	415.50		

16.3 Monika Schmidt runs a fitness centre "Tone Up" based in the town. "Tone Up" is incorporated as a limited company and is VAT-registered. Monika also uses a room in her house as an office for business purposes; the telephone bills for her home line are apportioned 30% business use, 70% domestic use.

During one week the following VAT invoices are received by the business:

supplier	goods/services supplied	net amount £	VAT £	gross amount £
Janus Cleaning	Cleaning of fitness centre	192.00	33.60	225.60
Ergo Sports	Rowing machine	1,250.00	218.75	1,468.75
Wyvern Motors	Mazda MX5 sports car	16,579.50	2,901.41	19,480.91
Peters Restaurant	Entertaining clients	230.60	40.35	270.95
BT	Home telephone line	126.76	22.18	148.94
BT	Business telephone line	346.74	60.67	407.41
Forte Hotels	Hotel room on business trip	240.50	42.08	282.58
Zap Supplies	Business stationery	46.50	8.13	54.63

You are to calculate

(a) the total VAT that the business will be able to claim as input tax

(b) the VAT that Monika will have to pay

16.4 When is the tax point in the following circumstances? All dates are in the same year.

(a) a VAT invoice dated 9 July is sent out on 9 July for services supplied on 9 July

(b) a VAT invoice dated 9 July is sent out on 10 July for services supplied on 6 July

(c) a VAT invoice dated 9 July is issued on 9 July for goods supplied on 30 June

(d) a VAT invoice dated 31 July is issued on 1 August for services supplied on 7 July

(e) a pro-forma invoice dated 31 July is issued on 31 July for goods ordered on 28 July

16.5 On the next three pages are examples of sales invoices issued by VAT registered businesses.

Are they valid VAT invoices? If not, why not?

SALES INVOICE

Keeping Sweet
Confectioners

29 Mintfield Street, Broadfield, BR7 4ER
Tel 01908 887634 Fax 01908 887239 Email sugarplum@sweet.goblin.com

Delia's Deli
36 The Arcade
Broadfield
BR1 4GH

invoice no	893823
account	3945
your reference	SP84
date/tax point	21 04 04

deliver to

as above

details	quantity	price	amount (excl VAT)	VAT rate %	VAT amount £
Cheesecake — summerfruit	20	5.50	110.00		19.25
Raspberry Pavlova	30	6.25	187.50		32.81

terms
Net monthly
Carriage paid
E & OE

Total (excl VAT)	297.50
VAT	52.06
TOTAL	349.56

SALES INVOICE

Trend Designs

Unit 40 Elgar Estate, Broadfield, BR7 4ER
Tel 01908 765365 Fax 01908 7659507 Email lisa@trend.u-net.com
VAT Reg GB 0745 4172 20

invoice to

```
'Tone Up' Sports Shop
38 The Arcade
Broadfield
BR1 4GH
```

invoice no	788776
account	4013
your reference	2067
date/tax point	21 05 04

deliver to

```
as above
```

details	quantity	price	amount (excl VAT)	VAT rate %	VAT amount £
'Surf Dood' T-shirts	20	5.50	110.00	17.5	19.25
'Surf Baby' tracksuits	15	15.50	232.50	17.5	40.69

terms
Net monthly
Carriage paid
E & OE

Total (excl VAT)	342.50
VAT	59.94
TOTAL	402.44

SALES INVOICE

Champ Cleaners
17 High Street, Broadfield, BR7 4ER
Tel 01908 283472 Fax 01908 283488

invoice to

Premier Insurance
49 Farrier Street
Broadfield
BR1 4LY

invoice no	**787906**
account	**3993**
your reference	**1956**

details	price
Office Cleaning 16 hrs	**104.00**

Total (excl VAT)	
VAT	
TOTAL	**122.20**

16.6 You work in the accounts office of a building firm. A trainee working on Purchase Ledger brings to your attention a number of low value invoices received from T Walker Joinery (which is registered for VAT). These invoices do not have the VAT amount specified – just the overall total. They *do* show the name and address of the supplier, the VAT registration number, the date of supply, the details of the goods and the VAT rate. The amounts are:

1   £18.21

2   £64.62

3   £94.00

4   £1.76

5   £93.94

6   £23.50

The trainee says "These are not valid VAT invoices – how are we supposed to enter them in the day book? There is no VAT amount shown."

You are to:

(a)   State whether the invoices are valid invoices, and if they are, why they are.

(b)   Show the trainee how to work out the VAT and the net amount by carrying out the appropriate calculation for all six invoices.

16.7 You work in the accounts department of a VAT-registered stationery supply business. You are asked to issue a pro-forma invoice to a customer who wishes to place an order but has not dealt with your firm before.

You have been asked by your supervisor to telephone the customer and to explain:

(a)   when the goods will be despatched

(b)   what a pro-forma invoice is

(c)   the VAT implications of a pro-forma invoice (the customer is also VAT-registered)

Write down in numbered points what you would say to the customer.

Note: if time permits this Activity could alternatively be carried out orally between student and tutor.

16.8 You work for a firm of accountants and are asked to advise a client, Jim Tredwell, who is planning to start an import/export agency for carpets and rugs. He has a number of questions:

(a)   "If I import rugs from India, do I have to pay tax to HM Customs & Excise? What rate would apply?"

(b)   "If I export a UK-manufactured Axminster carpet to a client in Oman, do I have to charge him VAT?"

(c)   "If I import a nylon/wool mix carpet from Belgium, do I have to pay tax to HM Customs & Excise? What rate would apply?"

(d)   "I have a client in Germany who is interested in high quality Wilton carpets. Do I have to charge her VAT?"

You are to state what your answer would be in each case. Ensure that you mention any difference made by VAT registration by the buyer or seller. Mr Tredwell is likely to have to register for VAT when he starts trading.

17 VAT RECORDS AND THE VAT RETURN

17.1 You work for Simpson & Co, Accountants, and have been given the VAT figures from the accounts of four clients.

You are to draw up a VAT control account for each client company to calculate the VAT due or reclaimable for the VAT period. You can use the format shown at the bottom of the page. If the final total is reclaimable VAT, it should be shown in brackets.

VAT FIGURES	Homer Ltd	Bart Ltd	Marge Ltd	Lisa Ltd
	£	£	£	£
Purchases Day Book	3,120.00	2,739.50	7,826.65	2,713.50
Sales Day Book	6,461.70	4,806.33	10,632.40	985.67
Credit notes received	530.50	231.60	987.60	156.70
Credit notes issued	245.79	542.77	876.34	87.23
Cash book purchases (non-credit)	567.90	765.91	145.78	978.67
Cash book sales (non-credit)	461.75	1,675.80	1,287.89	568.23
Petty cash book purchases	15.95	21.67	45.78	24.55
EU Acquisitions	796.30	nil	4,875.89	nil
VAT overpaid previous period	nil	345.78	654.89	78.60
VAT underpaid previous period	34.87	nil	637.98	nil
Bad debt relief	156.67	476.50	nil	65.50

VAT deductible (input tax)	VAT payable (output tax)
Purchases Day Book VAT total, *less* any credit notes received	Sales Day Book VAT total, *less* any sales credit notes issued
Cash Book – items not in Purchases Day Book	Cash Book – items not in Sales Day Book
Petty Cash Book – VAT on small expenses	
Acquisitions from EU states	Acquisitions from EU states
Corrections of errors from previous periods (not exceeding £2,000 net)	Corrections of errors from previous periods (not exceeding £2,000 net)
Bad debt relief	
= TOTAL TAX DEDUCTIBLE	= TOTAL TAX PAYABLE
	less TOTAL TAX DEDUCTIBLE
	equals TAX PAYABLE/(RECLAIMABLE)

17.2 In your work for Simpson & Co you have been asked to sort out the VAT Return of Damon Driver, a local businessman who has set up a computer equipment firm in the town. He has presented you with two box files of invoices, one marked 'Purchases/expenses' and the other marked 'Sales'. He says he has been 'so busy' that he hasn't had time to sort them out. You make a list of the invoices as follows:

PURCHASES/EXPENSES				SALES			
Supplier	net £	VAT £	gross £	Customer	net £	VAT £	gross £
Amax Machines	234.56	41.04	275.60	B Keaton	56.00	9.80	65.80
Electra Limited	5,467.80	956.86	6,424.66	C Chaplin	678.00	118.65	796.65
Microhard PLC	9,567.90	1,674.38	11,242.28	Laurel College	45,786.90	8,012.70	53,799.60
Peach Computers	5,278.89	923.80	6,202.69	Hardy & Co	17,678.50	3,093.73	20,772.23
Elsa Products	560.00	98.00	658.00	A Sim	1,250.00	218.75	1,468.75
IPM Computers	19,780.00	3,461.50	23,241.50	T Thomas	16,900.00	2,957.50	19,857.50
				E Sykes Ltd	12,500.00	2,187.50	14,687.50
				H Jacques	3,467.80	606.86	4,074.66
				V Singh	450.00	78.75	528.75
				L San	400.00	70.00	470.00
				A Larsen	125.00	21.87	146.87
				Z Zidane	780.50	136.58	917.08
				M Santos	56.00	9.80	65.80

Damon tells you that these are all the credit transactions for the quarter. He also mentions:

- he has made cash sales of £940 (including VAT) and incurred petty cash expenses of £76.37 (including VAT)

- there were no EU acquisitions, corrections, bad debts, or credit notes issued or received

You are to:

(a) total the money columns of the invoice listings in the above table

(b) construct a VAT control account (see the previous page for the format)

(c) state what figures you would transfer to the VAT 100 by completing the schedule below

VAT due on sales and other outputs	
VAT reclaimed on purchases	
VAT due/reclaimable	
Total value of sales and other outputs (excluding VAT)	
Total value of purchases and other inputs (excluding VAT)	

17.3   Julie Roberts is managing director of Pretty Woman Limited, a company which manufactures cosmetic accessories. The business is VAT-registered and submits its VAT Return quarterly at the end of March, June, September and December.

The business address is Unit 17 Everbeech Estate, Newtown, NW3 5TG. The VAT Registration number is 454 7106 51.

You work in the accounts department of Pretty Woman Limited and have been given the task of completing the VAT Return for the quarter ending 31 December of the current year.

You have collected the following data from the manual accounting records.

SALES DAY BOOK SUMMARY	standard-rated sales	VAT	total sales
	£	£	£
October	2,567.89	449.38	3,017.27
November	2,675.90	468.28	3,144.18
December	3,456.89	604.95	4,061.84

PURCHASES DAY BOOK SUMMARY	standard-rated purchases	VAT	total purchases
	£	£	£
October	1,456.90	254.95	1,711.85
November	3,456.20	604.83	4,061.03
December	1,490.25	260.79	1,751.04

CASH BOOK & PETTY CASH BOOK – NON CREDIT ITEMS (October - December)	net	VAT	total
	£	£	£
Cash sales	1,245.67	217.99	1,463.66
Petty cash expenses	67.80	11.86	79.66

ADDITIONAL INFORMATION

- Acquisitions from the EU for the period amounted to £850.70 net (VAT due of £148.87).

- Sales credit notes issued during the quarter amount to £345.70 + £60.49 VAT = £406.19.

- Credit notes received from suppliers amount to £400.00 + £70.00 VAT = £470.00.

- Bad debts written off during the year are:

  - £528.75 (invoice due 15 March, goods supplied 14 February)

  - £693.21 (invoice due 20 August, goods supplied 20 July)

  These invoice totals include VAT.

- In the previous VAT quarter there were two small errors in the accounts: output (sales) tax was underpaid by £44.50 and input tax (purchases) was over-estimated by £55.50.

You are to:

(a)   Complete the VAT Control Account (format shown below) for the October - December quarter.

(b)   Complete the VAT 100 form shown on the next page, ready for Julie Roberts' signature. Note that the year is shown as 'XX'; in reality the year would be shown as two digits.

VAT control account			
VAT deductible: input tax	£	**VAT payable: output tax**	£
Purchases Day Book		Sales Day Book	
less credit notes		less credit notes	
Cash Book		Cash Book	
Petty Cash Book			
EU Acquisitions		EU Acquisitions	
Correction of error		Correction of error	
Bad debt relief			
TOTAL INPUT TAX		TOTAL OUTPUT TAX	
		less TOTAL INPUT TAX	
		equals VAT DUE	

SPECIMEN

HM Customs and Excise

For the period
01 10 XX to 31 12 XX

625 454 7108 51 100 03 99 Q25147

PRETTY WOMAN LIMITED
17 EVERBEECH ESTATE
NEWTOWN
NW3 5TG

Your VAT Office telephone number is 01905 855600

Registration Number	Period
454 7108 51	12 XX

You could be liable to a financial penalty if your completed return and all the VAT payable are not received by the due date.

Due date: 31 01 XX

For Official Use

Before you fill in this form please read the notes on the back and the VAT leaflet *"Filling in your VAT return"*. Fill in all boxes in ink, and write 'none' where necessary. Don't put a dash or leave any box blank. If there are no pence write "00" in the pence column **Do not** enter more than one amount in any box.

For official use			£	p
	VAT due in this period on **sales** and other outputs	1		
	VAT due in this period on **acquisitions** from other **EC Member States**	2		
	Total VAT due (the sum of boxes 1 and 2)	3		
	VAT reclaimed in this period on **purchases** and other inputs (including acquisitions from the EC)	4		
	Net VAT to be paid to Customs or reclaimed by you (**Difference between boxes 3 and 4**)	5		
	Total value of **sales** and all other outputs excluding any VAT. **Include your box 8 figure**	6		00
	Total value of **purchases** and all other inputs excluding any VAT. **Include your box 9 figure**	7		00
	Total value of all **supplies** of goods and related services, excluding any VAT, to other **EC Member States**	8		00
	Total value of all **acquisitions** of goods and related services, excluding any VAT, from other **EC Member States**	9		00

Retail schemes. If you have used any of the schemes in the period covered by this return, enter the relevant letter(s) in this box.

If you are enclosing a payment please tick this box.

DECLARATION: You, or someone on your behalf, must sign below.

I, ...declare that the
(Full name of signatory in BLOCK LETTERS)
information given above is true and complete.

Signature ....Date ....19...............

A false declaration can result in prosecution.

L

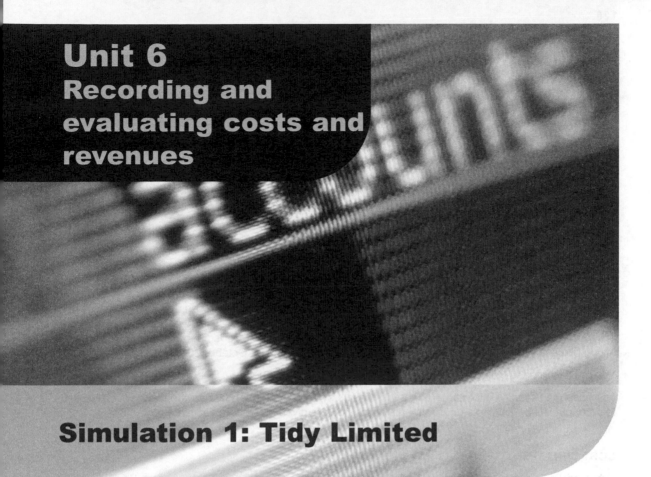

Unit 6
Recording and evaluating costs and revenues

Simulation 1: Tidy Limited

NVQ Element coverage

6.1 record and analyse information relating to direct costs and revenues

6.2 record and analyse information relating to the allocation, apportionment and absorption of overhead costs

6.3 prepare and evaluate estimates of costs and revenues

Scenario and contents

This simulation is based on Tidy Limited, a company which manufactures metal shelf units for use in offices. The tasks include:

■ calculation of Economic Order Quantity and stock levels

■ completion of stores ledger account

■ completion of cost ledger data entry sheets

■ calculation and analysis of wages

■ calculation of overhead absorption rates

■ assessment of overhead apportionment and absorption methods

■ analysis of cost behaviour

■ calculation of break-even point and margin of safety

■ capital investment appraisal using payback period and net present value

Suggested time allocation: four hours plus fifteen minutes reading time

SIMULATION 1
TIDY LIMITED

THE SITUATION

INTRODUCTION

Your name is John Raymond.

You have recently started work as an accounts assistant for Tidy Limited, a company which manufactures metal shelf units for use in offices. The administration of the firm is being reviewed and some changes are being considered. So that you may understand the present system and assist with the review, you are asked to complete various tasks. The financial year end for Tidy Limited is 31st October. The review is taking place in April and May 2004, half way through the year to 31st October 2004.

You are reporting to Helen Jones, a senior in the accounts department.

You have the following information about the present system and further data for the tasks you are asked to carry out will be available on documents which you are given in the data section.

COST CENTRES

Tidy Limited is organised into three production cost centres: Construction, Painting and Packing. In all three production cost centres the work is carried out by direct employees of Tidy Limited. There are two service cost centres: Stores and Administration.

THE PRESENT COST ACCOUNTING SYSTEM

Tidy Limited uses the weighted average method of valuation for stocks and for issues of materials from stores to work in progress.

Sheet metal and metal frames are treated as direct materials, all other materials (eg paint, rivets, small fittings, packing materials) being treated as indirect.

Overheads are absorbed on the basis of direct labour hours, separate rates being calculated for each of the three production cost centres. Any over or under absorption of overheads is transferred to the Profit and Loss Account at the end of the year.

VAT on purchases can be ignored in the costing records, as it can all be reclaimed.

The cost coding system for Tidy Limited includes the following codes:

Cost Centre Codes

CP10	Construction
CP20	Painting
CP30	Packing
CS40	Stores
CS50	Administration

[handwritten annotations: "PROD ⁿ" bracketing Construction/Painting/Packing; "SERVICE" bracketing Stores/Administration]

Expenditure Codes

M100	Direct Materials
M200	Indirect Materials
W300	Direct Wages
W400	Indirect Wages

TASKS TO BE PERFORMED

Section 1

1   Refer to the Memo dated 27 April 2004 from Helen Jones on page 128 and write a reply using the stationery on page 129.

2   Using the relevant documents from those relating to various materials on pages 130 to 132, complete the stores ledger account on page 133. You are reminded that the company uses the weighted average method of valuation. Assume that the supplier raises the invoice on the same day as delivery.

3   Using your answer to Task 2 and the documents relating to various materials on pages 130 to 132, complete the cost ledger data entry sheet on page 134.

4   Refer to the internal policy document on page 135 and the timesheets for three employees on page 136. Complete the calculation and analysis of gross wages for these employees on page 137. Read Task 5 below before commencing this task.

5   Using the stationery on page 138, write a Memo to Helen Jones, relating to any matters of uncertainty and assumptions you have had to make in Task 4 above.

6   Refer to the Memo from Helen Jones, dated 29 April 2004, on page 139 together with the attached notes on pages 139 to 140. Following the instructions given by Helen Jones, complete the schedules relating to overheads on page 141.

7   Using the stationery on page 142, write a Memo to Helen Jones stating whether you consider the revised methods of apportionment and absorption of overheads are an improvement on the previous system, giving brief reasons.

8   Using your answer to Task 6, complete the schedule for the six months ended 30 April 2004 on page 142, to show the total cost of 7,460 shelf units and the unit cost.

Section 2

The managers of Tidy Ltd are considering reducing the selling price of the shelf unit and also looking at the possibility of introducing new products. You are required to carry out some calculations in order to assist with these decisions.

9   Refer to the Memo from Helen Jones dated 30 April 2004 on page 143 and carry out the required calculations.

10   Refer to the Memo from Helen Jones dated 28 May 2004 on page 147 and carry out the required calculations.

MEMORANDUM

To: John Raymond

From: Helen Jones

Date: 27 April 2004

Subject: Stock policies

As part of our review, we have been asked to look at stock policies and, to help with my report, I would like you to answer the following questions:

(1) One of our materials is a spray paint, used to finish the products. The demand for this paint is 7,500 litres per year (assume this is at a steady rate through 50 weeks). When it is ordered, the paint usually arrives 2 weeks later. The cost of making an order is £20 and the cost of keeping one litre in stock for the year is £1. We need to keep a buffer stock sufficient for 1 week.

- What would you recommend as the Economic Order Quantity for the paint?

- What is the minimum (buffer stock) level?

- At what level should it be reordered?

- What maximum level would you set for this item of stock?

(2) The Manager considers that it might be possible to use Just-in-Time stock control for our metal sheets and frames.

- Can you explain briefly what this means?

- What are the main advantages?

- What are the main problems?

MEMORANDUM

To:

From:

Date:

Subject:

BALANCES EXTRACTED FROM STORES LEDGER

STOCK BALANCES AS AT 20 APRIL 2004

Code	Quantity	Unit Price	Total
108	95 boxes	£7.20 per box	£684.00
302	470 litres	£10.30 per litre	£4841.00
307	55 rolls	£8.00 per roll	£440.00

MATERIALS REQUISITION

DATE: 20/4/04   DEPT: CP30   NUMBER: 6342

CODE	DESCRIPTION	QUANTITY REQUIRED
307	Paksecure Tape	10 rolls

AUTHORISED: T. Hume

MATERIALS REQUISITION

DATE: 20/4/04   DEPT: CP10   NUMBER: 6343

CODE	DESCRIPTION	QUANTITY REQUIRED
101	Metal Sheets	250 sheets

AUTHORISED: M. Turner

MATERIALS REQUISITION

DATE: 21/4/04   DEPT: CP20   NUMBER: 6344

CODE	DESCRIPTION	QUANTITY REQUIRED
302	Spray paint (grey)	40 litres

AUTHORISED: R. Patton

MATERIALS REQUISITION

DATE: 22/4/04   DEPT: CP10   NUMBER: 6345

CODE	DESCRIPTION	QUANTITY REQUIRED
101	Metal Sheets	320 sheets

AUTHORISED: M. Turner

MATERIALS REQUISITION

DATE: 24/4/04   DEPT: CP10   NUMBER: 6346

CODE	DESCRIPTION	QUANTITY REQUIRED
108	Rivets	10 boxes

AUTHORISED: M. Turner

SALES INVOICE

Metafine Limited

Unit 8 Hall Road Industrial Estate, Newton, NN3 4BH
Tel 01906 765365 Fax 01906 7659112 Email john@metafine.goblin.com
VAT Reg GB 228 6654 78

invoice to

```
Tidy Limited
Victoria Road
Deans Hill
NN22 2QH
```

invoice no	3351
account	4018
your reference	286
date/tax point	21 04 04

deliver to

```
as above
```

details	quantity	price	amount (excl VAT)	VAT rate %	VAT amount £
Metal Sheets. Spec 101.	600	19.73	11,838.00	17.5	2,071.65

Total (excl VAT)	11,838.00
VAT	2,071.65
TOTAL	13,909.65

terms
Net 30 days

STORES LEDGER ACCOUNT

Material: Metal sheet
Code: 101

Unit: 1 sheet
Maximum control level: 1,000
Minimum control level: 150
Re-order level: 750
Re-order quantity: 600

DATE	RECEIPTS			ISSUES			STOCK BALANCE		
	Quantity	Unit Price £	Total £	Quantity	Unit Price £	Total £	Quantity	Unit Price £	Total £
17.04.04							350	18.32	6,412

COST LEDGER DATA ENTRY SHEET

Week ending   24 April 2004

Cost centre code	Expenditure code	Amount to be debited £
CP10	M100	
CP20	M100	
CP30	M100	
CP10	M200	
CP20	M200	
CP30	M200	
CS40	M200	
CS50	M200	
Total (check to documents)		

INTERNAL POLICY DOCUMENT

Issued: 30 November 2003

Subject: PRODUCTION WAGES

Construction Department

Direct workers in this department are paid a basic wage of £150 per week, plus a piecework rate of £5 per unit completed.

For example: a worker who makes 10 units earns £150 + £50.

The whole of this amount is treated as direct wages, unless the worker is absent from work, in which case £30 per day's absence is treated as overheads.

Painting Department

Direct workers in this department are paid a basic wage of £250 per 38 hour week. They are also paid a bonus of £6 per hour saved. The standard time allowed is 20 minutes per shelf unit.

The whole of the basic wage is treated as direct wages, unless the worker is absent from work, in which case £50 per day's absence is treated as overheads. The bonus is treated as indirect.

Packing Department

Direct workers are paid on an hourly basis at £6 per hour, up to 40 hours a week. Additional hours worked are paid at time and a half.

TIMESHEET

DEPARTMENT: Construction

EMPLOYEE: E. Fowler   WEEK ENDING: 24/4/04

	MON	TUE	WED	THUR	FRI	TOTAL
HOURS: Construction	7.5	8	8	8	7.5	39
Absent sick						
Holiday						
Training						
Total Hrs.						
Units Produced	4	6	5	6	5	26

TIMESHEET

DEPARTMENT: Painting

EMPLOYEE: R. Patton   WEEK ENDING: 24/4/04

	MON	TUE	WED	THUR	FRI	TOTAL
HOURS: Painting	8	8	8	8	6	38
Absent sick						
Holiday						
Training						
Total Hrs.						
Units Painted	25	25	26	28	16	120

TIMESHEET

DEPARTMENT: Packing

EMPLOYEE: L. Rigg   WEEK ENDING: 24/4/04

	MON	TUE	WED	THUR	FRI	TOTAL
HOURS: Packing	6	8.5	8	8	8	38.5
Absent sick						
Holiday						
Training	2.5					
Total Hrs.						
Units Packed	21	32	31	32	30	146

+ 2.5hr
= 41hr

CALCULATION AND ANALYSIS OF GROSS WAGES

Calculation

NAME	COST CENTRE CODE		AMOUNT
E. Fowler	CP10	BASIC	150
"	"	PIECEWORK	130
		TOTAL	280
R. Patton	CP20	BASIC	250
"	"	BONUS	12
		TOTAL	262
L. Rigg	CP30	BASIC	240
"	"	OVERTIME	·9
		TOTAL	249

Analysis NAME	COST CENTRE CODE	EXPENDITURE CODE	AMOUNT
E. Fowler	CP10	W300	280
"	"	W400	
R. Patton	CP20	W300	250
"	"	W400	12
L. Rigg	CP30	W300	225
"	"	W400	9 + 15
		TOTAL	791

MEMORANDUM

To:

From:

Date:

Subject:

MEMORANDUM

To: John Raymond

From: Helen Jones

Date: 29 April 2004

Subject: Overheads

Part of our review concerns overheads - apportionment and absorption. As you know, we absorb overheads on labour hours in all three production departments at present, but in the painting department the spray machines are automatic, once set up, so I consider the work to be machine intensive. Also some overheads have been shared equally between the cost centres up to now and I think this could be improved. I started working on all this, but I would like you to finish it and I attach my notes so far.

I did set up the schedules we need - please complete them.

NOTES - OVERHEADS

1 Half year 1/11/03 to 30/4/04 nearly completed.

Budgeted overheads for 6 months = £131,000

Department	budgeted overheads after allocation & apportionment	Direct Labour Hours
Construction	£52,000	12,500 hrs
Painting	£44,000	2,500 hrs
Packing	£35,000	1,875 hrs

Assume ACTUAL FIGS. for 6 months to 30/4/04 will be as estimated at 27/4/04:

<u>Actual direct labour hrs</u>

Construction	12,360 hrs
Painting	2,460 hrs
Packing	1,910 hrs

Actual overhead expenditure
for 6 months to 30/4/04 = £132,800.

2 Half year 1/5/04 to 31/10/04 about to start.

Budgeted overheads for 6 months = £131,000, consisting of:

Allocated overhead	Cost Centre
£4,400	CP10
£13,000	CP20
£2,200	CP30
£22,000	CS40
£32,400	CS50

and overheads to be apportioned - improve method?

Heat, light, maintenance of buildings	£18,000
Depreciation and maintenance of machines	£24,000
Other overheads (mainly related to number of staff in dept.)	£15,000

Information available

	CP10	CP20	CP30	CS40	CS50
Floor area (sq. metres)	220	90	50	140	100
NBV of machines(£000s)	140	180	40	30	10
Number of employees	13	3	2	4	8
Administration work (% of total)	50	30	15	5	–
Material requisitions (% of total)	55	25	20	–	–

3 ABSORPTION – CHANGE BASIS FOR PAINTING DEPT. TO MACHINE HOURS. PLANNED MACHINE HOURS = 4,000 HRS. FOR 6 MONTHS.

Construction and Packing - labour hours as in (1).

OVERHEADS SUMMARY FOR FIRST HALF YEAR

Period covered: 1/11/03 to 30/4/04

	CP10	CP20	CP30
Budgeted overheads	52,000	44,000	35,000
Planned labour hours	12,500	2,500	1,875
Absorption rate	4·16	17·60	18·67
Actual labour hours	12,360	2,460	1,910
Amount absorbed	51,417·60	43,296	35,659·70

Total amount absorbed	130,373·30
Total actual overheads	132,800
*Over/under absorption	2,426·70

The corresponding entry in the Profit & Loss Account will be *Debit/Credit.
*Delete where not applicable.

OVERHEADS BUDGET FOR SECOND HALF YEAR

Period covered: 1/5/04 to 31/10/04

	CP10	CP20	CP30	CS40	CS50	TOTAL
Allocated overheads	4,400	13,000	2,200	22,000	32,400	74,000
Heat, light, maintenance of buildings	6,600	2,700	1,500	4,200	3,000	18,000
Depreciation and maintenance of machines	8,400	10,800	2,400	1,800	600	24,000
Other overheads	6,500	1,500	1,000	2,000	4,000	15,000
Reapportion: Administration	20,000	12,000	6,000	8,000	(40,000)	
Stores	17,600	8,000	6,400	(32,000)		
TOTAL	63,500	48,000	19,500			
Absorption basis	12,500 hrs	4,000 hrs	1,875 hrs			
Absorption rate	$\frac{63,500}{12,500}$	$\frac{48,000}{4,000}$	$\frac{19,500}{1,875}$			

$\frac{48,000}{4,000 \text{ hrs}} = £12\,p/\text{hour}$

MEMORANDUM

To:

From:

Date:

Subject:

_____

Tidy Ltd

Schedule of costs for the first half year: 6 months ended 30 April 2004

Units produced: 7,460

	£
Direct material: metal sheets	288,702
Direct material: metal frames	43,641
Direct labour	120,282
Overheads absorbed	_____
Total cost	_____
Unit cost	_____

MEMORANDUM

To: John Raymond

From: Helen Jones

Date: 30 April 2004

Subject: Cost behaviour

We have been asked to sort out the costs according to whether they are variable, semi-variable or fixed and then do some projections using marginal costing. Here is a table showing the actual costs for the first half year split into the two quarters, followed by a list of tasks for you to carry out. I attach answer sheets to be returned to me.

Tidy Ltd

<u>Schedule of costs for the first half year: 6 months to 30 April 2004</u>

	3 months to 31 Jan 2004	3 months to 30 April 2004
Units produced	3,700	3,760
	£	£
Direct material: metal sheets	143,190	145,512
Direct material: metal frames	21,645	21,996
Direct labour	60,000	60,282
Actual overheads	66,400	66,400

Tasks

(a) Identify the behaviour of each cost and calculate the variable costs per unit and the fixed part of any semi-variable costs.

(b) Calculate the costs of making 4,000 shelf units per quarter (assuming the same level and behaviour of costs).

(c) Using the current selling price of £100 per shelf unit, calculate the contribution per unit and hence the break-even number of units to be made and sold per quarter. Assuming 4,000 units to be made and sold, calculate the percentage margin of safety.

(d) Using a reduced selling price of £80 per shelf unit, calculate the contribution per unit and hence the break-even number of units to be made and sold per quarter. Still assuming the same level and behaviour of costs and 4,000 units to be made and sold, calculate the percentage margin of safety and the profit per quarter.

(e) Comment briefly on the methods used and the results of these calculations — a decision is to be made about whether to reduce the selling price to £80.

Task 9: answer sheets to be returned to Helen Jones when completed

Cost behaviour analysis

(a)   Direct material:

Metal sheets

Metal frames

Direct labour

Overheads

(b)   Units produced: 4,000

	£ Fixed	£ Variable	£ Total
Direct material: metal sheets			
Direct material: metal frames			
Direct labour			
Actual overheads			
Total			

(c)   Contribution per unit if selling price is £100 per unit:

Break-even number of units

Margin of safety

Percentage margin of safety

(d)   Contribution per unit if selling price is £80 per unit

Break-even number of units

Margin of safety

Percentage margin of safety

Profit calculation:

Number of units made and sold: 4,000

Sales revenue   _____

Less: Total costs for 4,000 units per quarter from (b)   _____

Profit per quarter   _____

Check this by the alternative method:

Total contribution from 4,000 units   _____

Less: fixed costs per quarter   _____

Profit per quarter   _____

(e) Comments:

MEMORANDUM

To: John Raymond

From: Helen Jones

Date: 28 May 2004

Subject: Capital investment appraisal

The managers are considering launching one or more new products to go with the shelf units, such as metal filing cabinets or cupboards for offices. Capital investment in machinery and equipment would be needed. We are considering the first 6 years for each product.

Filing cabinets: initial investment would be £140,000 and residual value (after 6 years) would be £25,000

Cupboards: initial investment would be £60,000 and residual value (after 6 years) would be £10,000

The expected cash inflows for the 6 years are shown in the table below. Initial investment and residual value* have already been entered.

Please calculate the payback period and the net present value for each product. Use a discount rate of 12%.

Add some brief comments on your results and explain briefly (without calculations) what is meant by 'internal rate of return'. I attach answer sheets to be returned to me.

	Filing cabinets £000s	Cupboards £000s	Discount factor (12%)
Year			
2004	(140)	(60)	1.000
2005	25	25	0.893
2006	45	25	0.797
2007	65	30	0.712
2008	70	30	0.636
2009	65	25	0.567
2010	55 + 25*	25 + 10*	0.507

Task 10: answer sheets to be returned to Helen Jones when completed

Payback period

Filing cabinets

Cupboards

Discounted cashflows:

Year	Filing cabinets £000s	Cupboards £000s
2004		
2005		
2006		
2007		
2008		
2009		
2010		
Net Present Value		

Comments:

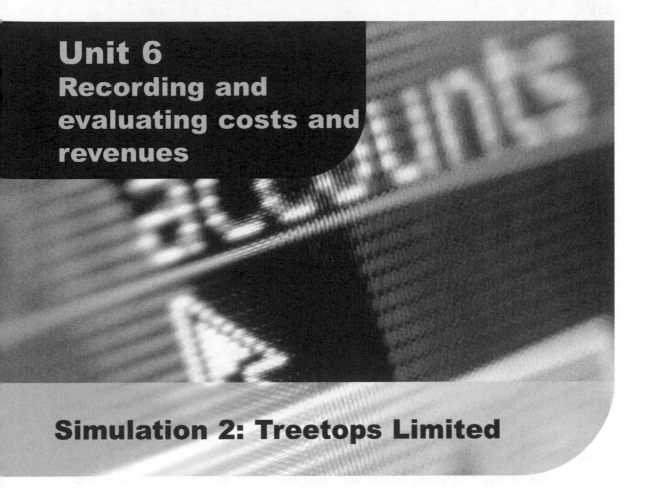

Unit 6
Recording and evaluating costs and revenues

Simulation 2: Treetops Limited

NVQ Element coverage

6.1 record and analyse information relating to direct costs and revenues

6.2 record and analyse information relating to the allocation, apportionment and absorption of overhead costs

6.3 prepare and evaluate estimates of costs and revenues

Scenario and contents

This simulation is based on Treetops Limited, a company which manufactures timber products. The tasks include:

■ calculation of overhead absorption rates

■ calculation of job costs and selling price

■ completion of a stores record card

■ recording of cost bookkeeping entries

■ investigating discrepancies and answering queries

■ profit maximisation with a limited resource

■ capital investment appraisal using payback period and net present value

This simulation is divided into two sections.

Suggested time allocation: four hours plus fifteen minutes reading time.

SIMULATION 2 TREETOPS LIMITED

SCENARIO

Your name is Carol Sims.

You are working in the Administration Section of Treetops Ltd, a company which manufactures timber products.

SECTION 1: DATA

Section 1 of this simulation is concerned with Treetops Frames Division, which manufactures timber frames for buildings. This division regularly produces basic frame sections in standard sizes and also makes frames to order, the customer having specified the sizes required.

All the data given for Section 1 relates to Treetops Frames Division. (Further data will be given for Section 2 on pages 152 to 153).

The customers of Treetops Frames Division are building contractors, who collect the frames they require. Treetops Frames Division does not own delivery vehicles.

The main material used by Treetops Frames Division is 100mm x 150mm pre-treated timber, which is purchased in 7m lengths. A stock of this material is kept in the yard, with the stock of finished frame sections.

Other materials used in the assembly of the frames include glue, brackets, nuts, bolts, screws etc. These are all kept in the Stores area of the factory and are referred to in general as "fixings" in the text which follows. The Stores area also contains stocks of packing materials and materials for the maintenance of the machinery.

There is no separate maintenance section. Production workers maintain their own machines.

Treetops Ltd's financial year end is 31st May. The activities are being carried out in May to July 2004 and relate to the year to 31st May 2005.

COST CENTRES (FRAMES DIVISION)

The cost centres are:

Code	Cost Centre
110	Cutting
120	Assembly
130	Goods Outward
140	Stores
150	Administration

Timber is issued from Stores to Cutting, where the sets of correct lengths to make the frames are cut.

Fixings are issued from Stores to Assembly, where the frames are put together in flat sections.

Customers collect frame sections from the Goods Outward section, where the additional fixings which will be required by the builder on site are identified. These are issued to Goods Outward from Stores, together with packing materials, and the Goods Outward worker ensures that the customer's order is packed and is complete.

The Administration Section deals with all aspects of administration of the business, including the accounting function. The Administration Section manages its own stocks of stationery and other office materials.

The Cutting, Assembly, Goods Outward and Stores cost centres come under the supervision of Kevin Grant, the Factory Manager, who joined Treetops Ltd fairly recently.

Toni White is an employee in the Administration Section.

THE COST ACCOUNTING SYSTEM (FRAMES DIVISION)

When a customer orders non-basic sized frames, job costing is used and the job price is calculated to give a profit margin of 30% of the selling price.

Cost Accounting Codes

Code	Type of cost	Includes
210	Direct Material	Timber only
220	Direct Wages	Work on production of frames in Cutting and Assembly only.
230	Variable Production Overhead	Indirect materials: fixings, packing and maintenance materials.
240	Fixed Production Overhead	Non-production work in Cutting and Assembly. All wages in Goods Outward and Stores. Factory Manager's salary, machine depreciation.
250	Administration Overhead	All administration costs.

After allocation and apportionment, totals for Production Overhead are obtained for Cutting and Assembly. This is done separately for Variable Production Overhead and Fixed Production Overhead.

Direct Labour hours in Cutting and Assembly are used for absorption of production overheads.

All other costs are collected in the administration cost centre and finally absorbed into the cost of sales as a percentage of the total production cost.

SECTION 1: TASKS

Task 1 relates to the budget, and determines the absorption rates. The same absorption rates will be used when job costing is applied, as for basic frame sections produced regularly.

Tasks 2 to 8 relate to the period commencing 1 June 2004, to which the budget applies.

1   The date is 11 May 2004. This task relates to calculation of the overhead absorption rates to be used in the year commencing 1 June 2004. You are given two schedules on pages 153 and 154. The first schedule was prepared by Kevin Grant on 5 May 2004 and the second was prepared by Toni White on 7 May 2004. They contain information about the budgeted production overheads and planned amounts of work for the year commencing 1 June 2004.

Using the information given in these schedules, you are required to calculate the total budgeted production overheads for each cost centre and the overhead absorption rates to be used. Your answers should be shown by completing the table on page 155.

2   It is now 15 June 2004, ie in the period for which the budgets have been prepared in Task 1. A customer, Fabro Ltd, has asked for an estimate for a set of frames of specified sizes. Refer to the Memo from Kevin Grant on page 156, the notes from Toni White on page 156 and your answer to Task 1 where relevant. You are required to complete the job estimate on page 157 and reply to Kevin Grant using the stationery on page 158.

3   An extract from the stock card for the timber material is shown on page 160. You are required to identify whether the method being used to value the issues from stock is FIFO, LIFO or weighted average. Continuing to use the method identified, complete the stock card for the period to 26 June 2004. You will need to refer to the documents on pages 158-159.

4   Using the stationery on page 161, write a Memo to Kevin Grant regarding:
     (i)   any queries you may have about the stock card for timber
     (ii)   a brief explanation of the possible reasons why the stock balance on the stock card may differ from the actual balance shown by a stocktake and the action that should be taken in this case.

5   Referring to your answers to tasks 1 and 3 and the job sheet for labour on page 161, complete the table on page 162. You are required to record the transfers of the costs of materials, labour, variable overheads and fixed overheads to the Job Account for Job J001FAB. Overheads are to be absorbed into the cost of the job on the basis of the actual hours worked.

6   Refer to the Memo from Kevin Grant, dated 6 July 2004, on page 162 and write a reply on the stationery on page 163. Your reply should answer all Kevin Grant's questions.

7   On 7 July 2004, you are investigating the Variable overhead expenditure for June 2004. Refer to the documents on pages 164 and 165, which you have extracted from the records. The documents relate to Indirect Materials for the week ended 19 June 2004. You are required to check the Cost Ledger Data Entry Sheet and to write a Memo, using the stationery on page 166, querying any unusual items or uncertainties in these documents.

8   This task relates to the administration overheads. You are reminded that all administration costs are collected in the Administration Cost Centre and absorbed into the Cost of Sales at the rate of 11% of Total Production Cost of Goods Sold. Refer to the Memo from Toni White, dated 8 July 2004, on page 167 and write a reply on the stationery on page 168.

SECTION 2: DATA AND TASKS

Section 2 data

Section 2 contains tasks to be carried out for Treetops Fencing Division. This division, which is completely separate from the Frames Division, manufactures fencing panels and wooden gates. The fencing panels are made in two sizes, large and small. The gates are made in one size only. The products are supplied direct to retailers, using subcontractors for the deliveries. Treetops Ltd does not currently own any delivery vehicles. The retailers expect the full range of products to be available, as their customers require specific quantities of matching panels and gates.

Section 2 Tasks

9   Refer to the memo from Toni White dated 12 May 2004 on page 169 and carry out the required calculations for the Fencing Division's products.

10   Refer to the Memo from Toni White dated 6 July 2004 on page 171 and carry out the required calculations to assist with the decision as to whether Treetops Ltd should purchase its own delivery vehicles. Reply to Toni White using the proforma on page 172.

TREETOPS FRAMES DIVISION
BUDGET FOR THE YEAR 1 JUNE 2004 TO 31 MAY 2005
PRODUCTION OVERHEADS

Prepared by: Kevin Grant   Date: 5 May 2004

Indirect Materials (allocated):

Cost Centre Code	Budget
110	£8,550
120	£116,550
130	£36,000

Indirect Wages (allocated):

Cost Centre Code	Budget
110	£10,325
120	£9,575
130	£16,000
140	£16,000

Planned Direct Labour Hours:

Cost Centre Code	Budget
110	7,500 hours
120	11,250 hours

TREETOPS FRAMES DIVISION

BUDGET FOR THE YEAR 1 JUNE 2004 TO 31 MAY 2005

PRODUCTION OVERHEADS

Prepared by: Toni White   Date: 7 May 2004

PRODUCTION OVERHEADS TO BE APPORTIONED

Type of cost	Amount	Basis of apportionment
Factory Manager's salary	£28,800	Number of employees
Depreciation of machines	£33,000	NBV of machinery
Stores (re-apportioned)		Number of Materials requisitions
Goods Outward (re-apportioned)		Equal parts to Cutting and Assembly

---

COST CENTRES (CODES)

	110	120	130	140
Numbers of employees	4	6	1	1
NBV of machines	£50,000	£20,000	£28,000	£12,000
Number of requisitions	900	360	540	-

Note

Everything is done for variable and fixed overheads separately, so that separate overhead absorption rates are calculated for Variable Overheads and Fixed Overheads, in each of the cost centres 110 (Cutting) and 120 (Assembly).

All overhead absorption rates are based on direct labour hours.

TREETOPS FRAMES DIVISION

BUDGET FOR THE YEAR 1 JUNE 2004 TO 31 MAY 2005

PRODUCTION OVERHEADS

Prepared by: Date:

cost centre code	110	120	130	140	
	Cutting £	Assembly £	Goods Outward £	Stores £	Total £
VARIABLE Indirect material					
Goods Outward re-apportioned					
Total	_____	_____			
	_____	_____			
Direct Labour hours	_____	_____			
VARIABLE OAR	_____	_____			
FIXED Indirect Wages					
Factory Manager					
Depreciation					
Stores re-apportioned					
Goods Outward re-apportioned					
TOTAL	_____	_____			
	_____	_____			
Direct Labour Hours as above					
	_____	_____			
FIXED OAR	_____	_____			

MEMORANDUM

To: Carol Sims

From: Kevin Grant

Date: 15 June 2004

Subject: Job no. J001FAB

I have calculated the requirements for this Job as follows. Please complete the attached estimate and let me know what the price will be, so that I can confirm the order with Fabro Ltd.

The job consists of 8 special sections:

SPECIAL SECTIONS		TIMBER (Code 210)	
Number Required	Size	Each section	Total for job
1	2m x 4m	2 lengths	2 lengths
3	3m x 4m	3 lengths	9 lengths
4	4m x 4m	4 lengths	16 lengths

Direct Labour: each special section takes 30 minutes in Cutting and 36 minutes in Assembly.

NOTES

Prepared by: Toni White   **Date:** 15 June 2004
Subject: Job Estimates

When estimating for jobs, use the following:
Expected cost of timber Code 210 is £10 per 7m length.
Budget rates to be charged for direct labour:
£8.80 per hour in the Cutting Department (110)
£8.55 per hour in the Assembly Department (120)

Administration overheads to be added at a rate of 11% of total Production Cost.
Profit margin to be 30% on selling price.

To be returned to Kevin

TREETOPS FRAMES DIVISION
JOB ESTIMATE

Prepared by:

Job Number: Customer Name:

	£	£

Direct Material: Timber

——————— lengths @ ———————

Direct Labour:

Cutting ——————— hours @ ———————

Assembly ——————— hours @ ———————

PRIME COST

Variable Production Overhead:

Cutting ——————— hours @ ———————

Assembly ——————— hours @ ———————

Fixed Production Overhead:

Cutting ——————— hours @ ———————

Assembly ——————— hours @ ———————

TOTAL PRODUCTION COST

Administration Overheads @ 11%

TOTAL COST

PROFIT (30% on selling price)

SELLING PRICE

MEMORANDUM

To:

From:

Date:

Subject:

MATERIALS REQUISITION

DATE: 18/6/04   DEPT: 110   Number: 070

CODE	DESCRIPTION	QUANTITY REQUIRED	JOB/PRODUCT
210	100mm x 150mm Timber (7m)	50	J032BSL

AUTHORISED: K. Grant

MATERIALS REQUISITION

DATE: 21/6/04   DEPT: 110   Number: 074

CODE	DESCRIPTION	QUANTITY REQUIRED	JOB/PRODUCT
210	100mm x 150mmTimber (7m)	200	P451 (basic)

AUTHORISED: K. Grant

MATERIALS REQUISITION

DATE: 22/6/04   DEPT: 110   NUMBER: 075

CODE	DESCRIPTION	QUANTITY REQUIRED	JOB/PRODUCT
210	100mm x 150mm Timber (7m)	12	J001FAB

AUTHORISED: K.Grant

MATERIALS REQUISITION

DATE: 23/6/04   DEPT: 110   NUMBER: 077

CODE	DESCRIPTION	QUANTITY REQUIRED	JOB/PRODUCT
210	100mm x 150mm Timber (7m)	16	J001FAB

AUTHORISED: K.Grant

MATERIALS RETURNED NOTE

DATE: 26/6/04   DEPT: 110   NUMBER: 038

CODE	DESCRIPTION	QUANTITY RETURNED	JOB/PRODUCT
210	100mm x 150mm Timber (7m)	2	J001FAB

AUTHORISED: K.Grant

TREETOPS FRAMES DIVISION
STOCK CARD

Material:	100mm x 150mm Timber (7m)
Code:	210
Unit:	1 length (7m)
Maximum level:	2,000
Minimum level:	500
Re-order level:	1,000
Re-order quantity:	1,000

Returns valued at same as last issue

DATE	RECEIPTS				ISSUES				STOCK		
	Document	Quantity	Unit Price £	Total £	Document	Quantity	Unit Price £	Total £	Quantity	Unit Price £	Total £
11/6/04									400	8.50	3,400
14/6/04	GRN089	1,000	9.00	9,000					1,000	9.00	9,000
15/6/04					067	250	8.50	2,125	150	8.50	1,275
									1,000	9.00	9,000
17/6/04	GRN090	1,000	9.10	9,100					1,000	9.10	9,100

MEMORANDUM

To:

From:

Date:

Subject:

TREETOPS FRAMES DIVISION

JOB SHEET

Job Number: J001FAB   **Customer:** Fabro Ltd.

Date	Cost Centre	Rate £	Name	Time Worked
22/6/04	110	8.80	P.Remy	45 minutes
22/6/04	110	8.80	S.Benn	1 hour
24/6/04	110	8.80	P.Remy	1 hour
24/6/04	110	8.80	S.Benn	1 hour
25/6/04	120	8.55	S.Lynn	1 hr 40 mins
25/6/04	120	8.55	T.Martinez	1 hr 40 mins
25/6/04	120	8.55	J.Abbey	1 hr 40 mins

Table of entries to record the transfer of the costs of materials, labour, variable production overheads and fixed production overheads to the Job Account for Job J001FAB

Account	Dr £	Cr £
Timber material (Stores control)		
Job Account: Job Number J001FAB		
Wages control		
Job Account: Job Number J001FAB		
Variable Production Overhead Control		
Job Account: Job Number J001FAB		
Fixed Production Overhead Control		
Job Account: Job Number J001FAB		
Total		

MEMORANDUM

To: Carol Sims

From: Kevin Grant

Date: 6 July 2004

Subject: Job J001FAB

I have looked at the costs of Job J001FAB and would like you to explain a few points to me:

1. What are the definitions of "Variable" overheads and "Fixed" overheads?

2. I have checked the rates for direct labour hours in Cutting and Assembly, but they are not the same per hour as the workers get paid. Toni said they were "inflated" for some reason due to holidays. Can you explain please?

3. The absorption rates are calculated separately for Cutting and Assembly. Can you tell me what is the benefit of this over having them all put together as if it was one department?

MEMORANDUM

To:

From:

Date:

Subject:

MATERIALS REQUISITION

DATE: 15/6/04   DEPT: 120   NUMBER: 068

CODE	DESCRIPTION	QUANTITY REQUIRED
307	Corner brackets @ £28 per box	50 boxes

AUTHORISED: K.Grant

MATERIALS REQUISITION

DATE: 16/6/04   DEPT: 110   NUMBER: 069

CODE	DESCRIPTION	QUANTITY REQUIRED
309	Saw blades @ £97 each	4 blades

AUTHORISED: K.Grant

MATERIALS REQUISITION

DATE: 18/6/04   DEPT: 110   NUMBER: 071

CODE	DESCRIPTION	QUANTITY REQUIRED
302	Heavy Plastic Packing Sheet @ £52 per roll	6 rolls

AUTHORISED: K.Grant

MATERIALS REQUISITION

DATE: 19/6/04   DEPT: 120   NUMBER: 072

CODE	DESCRIPTION	QUANTITY REQUIRED
305	Nuts & Bolts @ £14 per box	20 boxes

AUTHORISED: K.Grant

MATERIALS REQUISITION

DATE: 19/6/04   DEPT: 130   NUMBER: 073

CODE	DESCRIPTION	QUANTITY REQUIRED
308	Packing Tape @ £22 per roll	10 rolls

AUTHORISED: K.Grant

COST LEDGER DATA ENTRY SHEET

Week ending: 19 June 2004

CODE		AMOUNT	
COST CENTRE	EXPENDITURE	TO BE DEBITED	TO BE CREDITED
		£	£
110	230	980	
120	230	1,400	
130	230	220	

MEMORANDUM

To:

From:

Date:

Subject:

MEMORANDUM

To: Carol Sims

From: Toni White

Date: 8 July 2004

Subject: Administration Overheads

I have been looking at the Administration Overhead Account for the month of June 2004. The total actual expenditure which has been coded to this account during June is £13,200 and the amount absorbed using the 11% rate is £11,880. I do not quite understand what this difference is and what caused it. Could you explain it to me, please? Also what double entry is needed to deal with it?

MEMORANDUM

To:

From:

Date:

Subject

MEMORANDUM

To: Carol Sims

From: Toni White

Date: 12 May 2004

Subject: Fencing Division production

There are three products made in the Fencing Division: large panels, small panels and gates.

Maximum production demand figures for these for the next quarter of the year are shown in the attached table. Skilled workers are required to operate some of the machinery used to cut the timber and there will be a shortage of hours available in the next quarter, which probably means the full production demand cannot be met. The total machine operating time available for the quarter will be 1,700 hours.

Please complete the attached table in order to show the production quantities that would maximise profit and add your comments, so that I can let the Fencing Production Manager know the results.

Table to be returned to Toni White when completed:

Treetops Fencing Division Production

	Small Panel	Large Panel	Gate
Quarterly demand (units)	4,000	6,000	500
Machine operating hours per unit	0.20	0.25	0.30
Selling price per unit	£30	£37	£53
Variable costs per unit	£18	£25	£32
Contribution per unit			
Contribution per unit per machine operating hour			
Ranking			
Production units for maximum profit			
Machine operating hours used			

Comments:

MEMORANDUM

To: Carol Sims

From: Toni White

Date: 6 July 2004

Subject: Fencing Division: delivery vehicles

The managers of the fencing division are considering whether it would be worthwhile to invest in their own delivery vehicles, instead of using subcontractors. The capital investment would amount to £150,000 and it is expected that cash savings of £50,000 per year would be made, after allowing for running costs.

The residual value of the vehicles after 4 years is estimated as £35,000. Taking this into account, with the initial investment and four years' savings, calculate the payback period for this project and the Net Present Value using a discount rate of 10%.

The discount factors you need are:

Year 1: 0.909

Year 2: 0.826

Year 3: 0.751

Year 4: 0.683

Use the proforma provided and comment briefly on the results.

Proforma

Payback and net present value calculations for delivery vehicles for 4 years

	Cash flow £000s	Cumulative cash flow £000s	Discount factor (10%)	Discounted cash flow £000s
Year 0			1.000	
Year 1			0.909	
Year 2			0.826	
Year 3			0.751	
Year 4			0.683	
Net Present Value				

Comments:

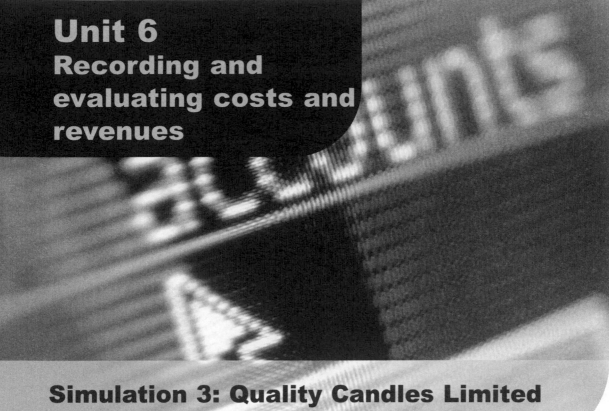

Unit 6
Recording and evaluating costs and revenues

Simulation 3: Quality Candles Limited
(adapted from AAT sample material) © AAT, 2003

NVQ Element coverage

6.1 record and analyse information relating to direct costs and revenues

6.2 record and analyse information relating to the allocation, apportionment and absorption of overhead costs

6.3 prepare and evaluate estimates of costs and revenues

Scenario and contents

This Simulation is based on Quality Candles Limited, a manufacturer of candles for the the general market. The tasks in the simulation involve:

■ completion of a stores record card

■ calculation and analysis of wages

■ calculation of overhead absorption rates

■ assessment of overhead apportionment methods

■ analysis of cost behaviour

■ calculation of breakeven point and margin of safety

■ capital investment appraisal using payback and net present value

Suggested time allocation: four hours plus fifteen minutes reading time.

SIMULATION 3
QUALITY CANDLES LIMITED

IMPORTANT NOTE

Part 1 tasks (2 hours) are on pages 174-176 and Part 2 tasks (2 hours) are on page 184.

SCENARIO

Your name is Bobby Forster and you work as the Accounts Assistant for Quality Candles Limited. The company manufactures candles of all kinds, including hand made candles. The candles are sold to wholesalers, to retailers, and direct to the public through the company's mail order division.

THE MANUFACTURING OPERATIONS

The manufacturing operations involve three production cost centres and two service cost centres.

Production cost centres	*Service cost centres*
Manufacturing	Stores
Painting and finishing	Maintenance
Packing	

THE TIME PERIOD COVERED BY THIS SIMULATION

The company's year-end is 31 December.

This simulation is concerned with activities during the quarter ending 31 December 2003, and with planning activities for the year ending 31 December 2004.

PART ONE: ELEMENT 6.1 TASKS

Recommended time for completion: one hour

1   Refer to the stores record card on page 188.

Complete this stores record card using the information from the materials documentation on page 189 and page 177. You will need to identify and apply the stock valuation method in use and you are advised that VAT is not entered in the cost accounting records.

Show the volume and value of the stock at the close of the week ending 10 October 2003. Any returns from production cost centres to stores are valued at the price of the most recent batch issued from stores.

2   Refer to the materials requisition note and materials returned note on page 189.

Complete the column headed 'Cost office use only' on each of the two documents.

3   Refer to your completed stores record card on page 188.

Prepare a memo for the general manager, drawing attention to any unusual issues concerning the stock levels for this item during the week. Your memo should highlight the issues, point out any possible consequences, and suggest any action that might be taken to prevent the unusual situations occurring. Use the blank memo form on page 190.

4   Refer to the internal policy document on page 178 and the piecework operation card on page 191.

Complete the piecework operation card using the information provided. You will need to do the following:

- Calculate the piecework payment for each day.
- Calculate any bonus payable for the day.
- Calculate the total wages payable for the day.
- Complete the analysis of total wages payable for the week.

5   Refer to the piecework operation card on page 191.

Identify any possible discrepancy in the activity data and write a memo to the supervisor, Roy Hart, explaining clearly what you think the discrepancy might be. Use the blank memo form on page 192.

PART ONE: ELEMENT 6.2 TASKS

Recommended time for completion: one hour

6   Refer to the memo on page 179.

Perform the production overhead allocation and apportionment exercise using the analysis sheet on page 193. You will see that the task has already been started in respect of indirect labour. The data that you have gathered is on pages 180 and 181.

7   Refer to the memo on page 181.

Calculate the production overhead absorption rates for 2004. You will need to make use of the following:

- The blank working paper on page 194.
- The data on pages 180 and 181.
- Your results for the total production department overhead for 2004 on page 193.

All absorption rates should be calculated to the nearest penny.

8   Refer to the memo on page 182.

Re-calculate the total production overhead for each production department, reversing the order of apportionment of the service department overheads. Use the working paper on page 195. You will need to do the following:

- Transfer your figures for total department overhead for all five departments from your overhead analysis sheet on page 193.

- Re-apportion the service department overheads, apportioning the stores costs first to the other four departments on the basis of the number of material requisitions. Then re-apportion the total overhead of the maintenance department to the three production departments, on the basis of maintenance hours.

Perform all calculations to the nearest £000.

9   Review your results from Task 8 and write a memo to the general manager. In your memo you should:

- comment on the effect of the change in method

- explain whether you think it is necessary to instigate a change in the method of re-apportionment of service department costs

Use the blank memo form on page 195.

10   Refer to the memo and the production overhead data on page 183.

Complete the journal entry form on page 196.

Write a memo to the production manager detailing any queries concerning the data and suggesting possible causes of any discrepancies you have identified. Use the blank memo form on page 196.

PART ONE DATA

SALES INVOICE
Threadshop Limited
25 Lyme Street, Taunton TA2 4RP
VAT Registration 254 1781 26

Date/tax point: 9 October 2003
Invoice number: T543
Your order: 47346

Invoice to:
Quality Candles Limited
2 Norman Lane
Winterbury
RT5 8UT

Description of goods/services	Total (£)
Candlewick thread, 200 metre rolls 80 rolls @ £2.38	190.40
Goods total	190.40
VAT @ 17.5%	33.32
Total due	223.72

Terms: net 30 days

Checked against GRN no 427
Date received: 9 October 2003
Signed: J Jones

INTERNAL POLICY DOCUMENT

Document no: 18

Subject: Wages

Issued: August 2003

Piecework scheme

A piecework scheme is to be introduced into the manufacturing department in order to reward efficient and productive operatives.

A piecework rate per batch of £0.50 will be paid for each batch of accepted output produced during a day.

In addition a bonus will be paid of 4 per cent of the piecework payment for any day on which the number of batches rejected by Quality Control is less than 5 per cent of the total number of batches produced.

A guaranteed daily wage of £50 is payable if the piecework payment + bonus amounts to less than £50 in any day.

Analysis of wages

Piecework payments and guaranteed daily wages paid will be treated as direct wages costs.

Bonus payments will be treated as indirect wages costs.

Discrepancies on piecework operation cards

The company wishes to pay wages and report labour rates promptly. Therefore employees will initially be paid for the total wages calculated according to the data contained on the weekly piecework operation card.

Any discrepancies on operation cards will be referred to the supervisor. Any alterations to wages will be agreed with the employee before adjustment is made to the next wage payment.

MEMO

To: Bobby Forster, Accounts Assistant
From: General Manager
Subject: Budgeted production costs for 2004
Date: 28 October 2003

As you know we have begun our budgetary planning exercise for 2004.

I understand that you have been working on the analysis of budgeted production costs. Could you please pull together all the information you have gathered and carry out the allocation and apportionment exercise for production overhead costs for 2004.

Thanks. Then we will have the necessary information that we need to calculate the pre-determined overhead absorption rates for 2004.

DATA FOR PRODUCTION OVERHEAD ANALYSIS FOR 2004

1 Summary of budgeted production costs for 2004

	£000
Direct materials	200
Indirect materials	40
Direct labour	420
Indirect labour:	
Manufacturing department	22
Painting and finishing department	14
Packing department	11
Stores	35
Maintenance	16
Rent and rates	105
Protective clothing	31
Power	40
Insurance	24
Heat and light	35
Depreciation	48
Other production overheads	15
Total budgeted production costs	1,056

2 Other data

	Manufacturing	Painting/ finishing	Packing	Stores	Maintenance
Direct materials cost (£000)	150	25	25	-	-
Floor area (000 sq metres)	30	10	16	8	6
Power usage (%)	50	10	30	5	5
Net book value of equipment (£000)	220	80	120	40	20
Maintenance hours (000)	7	4	3	1	-
Materials requisitions (000)	18	10	9	-	11
Direct labour hours (000)	20	28	10	-	-
Machine hours (000)	200	14	90	-	-

3   **Company procedures for the allocation and apportionment of production overheads**

- 30 per cent of the total indirect materials cost is apportioned to stores and 30 per cent to maintenance. The remaining 40 per cent is apportioned to the production departments according to the direct materials cost.

- Rent and rates and heating and lighting costs are apportioned according to the floor area occupied by each department.

- The cost of protective clothing is allocated to the manufacturing department.

- Power costs are apportioned according to the power usage in each department.

- Insurance and depreciation costs are apportioned according to the net book value of equipment in each department.

- Other production overheads are apportioned equally to the production departments.

- The total cost of the maintenance department is apportioned to the other four departments according to the number of maintenance hours.

- After a charge has been received from the maintenance department, the total cost of the stores department is apportioned to the three production departments according to the number of material requisitions.

- All calculations are rounded to the nearest £000.

MEMO

To: Bobby Forster, Accounts Assistant
From: General Manager
Subject: Pre-determined overhead absorption rates
Date: 28 October 2003

Many thanks for all your hard work on the overhead analysis.

Could you please now use the results of your analysis to calculate overhead absorption rates for the three production departments for 2004. We have decided that the most appropriate bases of absorption will be as follows:

- Manufacturing department: machine hour rate;
- Painting and finishing department: labour hour rate;
- Packing department: machine hour rate.

Thanks for your help.

MEMO

To: Bobby Forster, Accounts Assistant
From: General Manager
Subject: Re-apportionment of service department costs
Date: 4 November 2003

I have been giving some thought to the method that we use to re-apportion the service department costs to the production departments.

As you know, at present it is our policy to apportion the maintenance costs to all cost centres before we re-apportion the total stores costs to the production cost centres.

I would like to see the effect of altering the order of re-apportionment of service department costs. Could you please rework the figures so that we can review the results?

Let me have the results and your views as soon as possible, please.

MEMO

To:	Bobby Forster, Accounts Assistant
From:	General Manager
Subject:	Overhead absorption for October 2003
Date:	8 November 2003

As you know it is company policy to accumulate the under or over-absorbed production overhead each month in an account maintained for this purpose.

The production overhead data for October 2003 has now been finalised.

Could you please complete the journal entry for the absorption of production overhead into the work in progress accounts and transfer any under or over absorption for the month. Complete the entries using the data provided, but please let the production manager know if you have any queries concerning the data.

SUMMARY OF PRODUCTION OVERHEAD DATA FOR OCTOBER 2003

	£
Actual production overhead incurred	15,800
Production overhead to be absorbed into work in progress	
Manufacturing department	18,500
Painting and finishing department	7,400
Packing department	8,300

PART TWO: ELEMENT 6.3 TASKS

Recommended time for completion: two hours.

11   Refer to the memo on page 185 (top) and prepare the necessary information in response to the General Manager's query. You will need to do the following:

Use the data on page 185 (bottom) and the working paper on pages 197-198 to identify the cost and revenue behaviour patterns to be used in your projections.

Use your identified cost and revenue behaviour patterns to complete the planned profit projection on page 198.

12   Refer to the memo on page 186 and answer the General Manager's queries. You will need to do the following:

(i)   Use your identified cost and revenue behaviour patterns, adjusted for the change in materials cost, to prepare a revised planned profit statement for December. Complete the profit statement on page 199. There is space for your workings at the bottom of this page.

(ii)   Calculate the breakeven point in terms of the number of cases to be sold in December if the bulk discount is accepted. Use the blank working paper on page 200 and round your answer up to the nearest number of whole cases. Also use the same working paper to calculate the margin of safety. Express your answer as a percentage of the increased planned activity for December.

(iii)   Prepare a memo to the General Manager evaluating the results of your calculations. Your memo should contain the following:

-       your comments on the resulting profit, breakeven point and margin of safety

-       a statement of any assumptions you have used in evaluating the proposal

Use the blank memo form on page 201.

13   Refer to the memo on page 187 and do the following:

(i)   Use the working paper on page 202 to calculate the payback period and the net present value of the proposed investment. Ignore inflation and perform all monetary calculations to the nearest £.

(ii)   Write a memo to the General Manager evaluating the proposal from a financial viewpoint and stating any assumptions you have made in your analysis. Use the blank memo form on page 203.

PART TWO DATA

MEMO

To: Bobby Forster, Accounts Assistant
From: General Manager
Subject: Mail order division: revised plan for December 2003
Date: 9 November 2003

Could you please prepare the revised cost and revenue plan for the mail order division for December.

The plan is to sell 6,800 cases of candles and we will base our projections on the cost and revenue behaviour patterns experienced during August to October.

Thanks for your help.

QUALITY CANDLES LIMITED: MAIL ORDER DIVISION

Actual results for August to October 2003

	August	September	October
Number of cases sold	7,000	6,200	5,900
	£	£	£
Candles cost	9,100	8,060	7,670
Packing materials cost	5,250	4,650	4,425
Packing labour cost	2,100	1,860	1,770
Packing overhead cost	5,400	5,240	5,180
Other overhead cost	2,500	*3,000	2,500
Total costs	24,350	22,810	21,545
Sales revenue	28,000	24,800	23,600
Profit	3,650	1,990	2,055

*   *Other overhead cost was £500 higher than usual during September owing to an unexpected machine breakdown which necessitated the hire of a packing machine to maintain production. This event will not recur in the future.*

MEMO

To: Bobby Forster, Accounts Assistant
From: General Manager
Subject: Mail order division: bulk discounts for December 2003
Date: 10 November 2003

Many thanks for your splendid work on the cost and revenue projections for December.

We are looking for opportunities to increase profit and we have just heard that we can obtain a bulk discount for packing materials in December if we increase our activity level to 7,600 cases for the month. This will mean that packing material unit costs will reduce by 20 per cent.

Could you please recalculate the profit projection for December if we decide to increase activity to take advantage of the discount?

Also, please calculate the breakeven point in terms of the number of cases to be sold in December if we make this change. I would also like to have a note of the margin of safety we will have.

Please let me have the results of your calculations and your comments on the outcome as soon as you can.

MEMO

To: Bobby Forster, Accounts Assistant
From: General Manager
Subject: Purchase of delivery vehicles for mail order division
Date: 12 November 2003

We are considering the purchase and operation of our own fleet of delivery vehicles at the end of this year.

The distribution manager informs me that we will be able to cancel our current delivery contract and as a result we will enjoy cash savings of £34,800 each year from 2004 onwards, after taking account of the vehicle operating costs.

The vehicles will cost us £90,000 and will have a resale value of £5,000 when they are sold at the end of 2007.

Can you please appraise this proposal from a financial viewpoint? I need to know the payback period and the net present value at our usual discount rate of 12 per cent. As you know our maximum required payback period for all capital projects is three years.

Please let me have the results as soon as possible.

PART ONE ANSWER PAGES

Task 1

STORES RECORD CARD

Materials description: Candlewick thread, 200 metre rolls   Maximum quantity: 400

Code no: CW728   Minimum quantity: 140
                Reorder level: 230
                Reorder quantity: 80

	Receipts				Issues				Stock balance		
Date 2003	Document number	Qty	Price per roll (£)	Total (£)	Document number	Qty	Price per roll (£)	Total (£)	Qty	Price per roll (£)	Total (£)
1 Oct									28	2.20	61.60
									26	2.30	59.80
									54		121.40
3 Oct					249	26	2.30	59.80			
						4	2.20	8.80			
						30		68.60	24	2.20	52.80
6 Oct	419	80	2.35	188.00					24	2.20	52.80
									80	2.35	188.00
									104		240.80

Task 2

MATERIALS REQUISITION

Department: Manufacturing

Document no: 252
Date: 08/10/2003

Code no	Description	Quantity	Cost office use only Value of issue (£)
CW728	Candlewick thread, 200m rolls	40	

Signature: Received by:

MATERIALS RETURNED

Department: Manufacturing

Document no: 75
Date: 10/10/2003

Code no	Description	Quantity	Cost office use only Value of issue (£)
CW728	Candlewick thread, 200m rolls	3	

Signature: Received by:

Task 3

MEMO

To:

From:

Subject:

Date:

Task 4

QUALITY CANDLES LIMITED

PIECEWORK OPERATION CARD

Operative name: Mary Roberts

Department: Manufacturing

Clock number: R27

Week beginning: 6 October 2003

	Mon	Tues	Wed	Thurs	Fri
Batches produced	120	102	34	202	115
Batches rejected	5	7	4	11	5
Batches accepted					
Rate per batch	£0.50	£0.50	£0.50	£0.50	£0.50
Piecework payment	£	£	£	£	£
Bonus payable	£	£	£	£	£
Total payable for day*	£	£	£	£	£

Total wages payable for week:

Direct wages   £

Indirect wages   £

Total wages   £

* Guaranteed daily wage of £50 is payable if piecework payment plus bonus amounts to less than £50.

Supervisor's signature: *A Peters*

Task 5

MEMO

To:
From:
Subject:
Date:

Task 6

PRODUCTION OVERHEAD ANALYSIS SHEET FOR 2004						
Production overhead item	Total £000	Manufacturing £000	Painting/ finishing £000	Packing £000	Stores £000	Maintenance £000
Indirect labour	98	22	14	11	35	16
Total departmental overheads						
Apportion maintenance total	–					( )
Apportion stores total	–				( )	
Total production dept overheads						

Task 7

WORKING PAPER

CALCULATION OF PRODUCTION OVERHEAD ABSORPTION RATES FOR 2004

Manufacturing department

Painting and finishing department

Packing department

Task 8

SAMPLE CALCULATIONS: WORKING PAPER						
Reversing the order of service department re-apportionments						
Production overhead item	Total £000	Manufacturing £000	Painting/ finishing £000	Packing £000	Stores £000	Maintenance £000
Total departmental overheads (from Task 6)						
Apportion stores total	–				( )	
Apportion maintenance total	–				–	( )
Total production dept overheads						

Task 9

MEMO

To:

From:

Subject:

Date:

_____

Task 10 **Journal entry for production overheads: October 2003**

Entries for overhead absorbed during the month

	Debit (£)	Credit (£)
Work in progress: manufacturing dept		
Work in progress: painting and finishing dept		
Work in progress: packing dept		
Production overhead control		

Entries for overhead under/over absorbed during the month

	Debit (£)	Credit (£)
Overhead over/under absorbed (P + L)		
Production overhead control		

MEMO

To:

From:

Subject:

Date:

PART TWO ANSWER PAGES

Task 11

WORKINGS FOR DETERMINATION OF REVENUE AND COST BEHAVIOUR PATTERNS

Sales revenue

Candles cost

Packing materials cost

Packing labour cost

Packing overhead cost

Other overhead cost

QUALITY CANDLES LIMITED: MAIL ORDER DIVISION

Planned results for December 2003

	December
Number of cases to be sold	
	£
Candles cost	
Packing materials cost	
Packing labour cost	
Packing overhead cost	
Other overhead cost	
Total costs	
Sales revenue	
Profit	

Space for workings

Task 12 (i)

QUALITY CANDLES LIMITED: MAIL ORDER DIVISION

Planned results for December 2003: increased activity

	December
Number of cases to be sold	7,600
	£
Candles cost	
Packing materials cost	
Packing labour cost	
Packing overhead cost	
Other overhead cost	
Total costs	
Sales revenue	
Profit	

Space for workings

Task 12 (ii)

QUALITY CANDLES LIMITED: MAIL ORDER DIVISION

Planned results for December 2003: increased activity

Calculation of breakeven point and margin of safety: working paper

Task 12 (iii)

MEMO

To:

From:

Subject:

Date:

_____

Task 13 (i)   Working paper for the financial appraisal of purchase of delivery vehicles

Year	Cashflow £	Discount factor @ 12%	Present value £
2003		1.000	
2004		0.893	
2005		0.797	
2006		0.712	
2007		0.636	

Net present value

Working space for calculation of payback period

Task 13 (ii)

MEMO

To:

From:

Subject:

Date:

_____

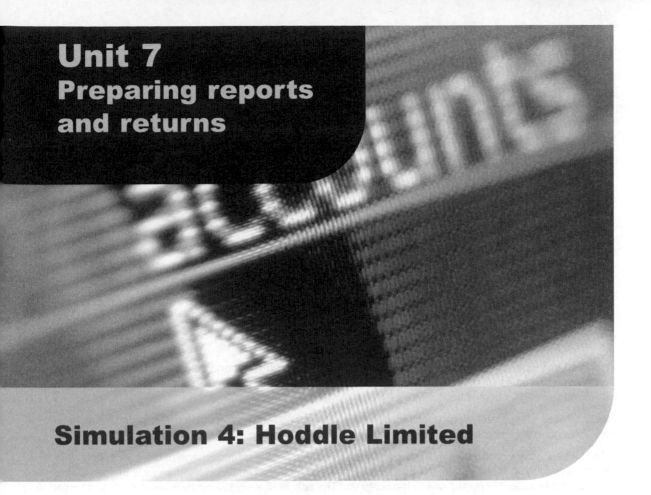

Unit 7
Preparing reports and returns

Simulation 4: Hoddle Limited

NVQ Element coverage

7.1 prepare and present periodic performance reports

7.2 prepare reports and returns for outside agencies

7.3 prepare VAT returns

Scenario and contents

This simulation is based on Hoddle Limited, a company which prints cards, brochures and booklets. Sometimes it contracts out work to Kelly Limited, another company in the same group. The tasks include:

- preparation of a VAT Return from the accounting records

- dealing with queries involving VAT

- consolidating the profit and loss accounts for Hoddle Ltd and Kelly Ltd

- preparing an internal report presenting key ratios and performance indicators

- preparation of an interfirm comparison form

Suggested time allocation: three hours plus fifteen minutes reading time

SIMULATION 4
HODDLE LIMITED

THE SITUATION

Your name is Sol Bellcamp and you work as an accounts assistant for a printing company, Hoddle Limited. Hoddle Limited is owned 100 per cent by another printing company, Kelly Limited. You report to the Group Accountant, Sherry Teddingham.

Hoddle Limited manufactures a wide range of printed materials such as cards, brochures and booklets. Most customers are based in the UK, but sales are also made to other countries in the European Union (EU). There are no exports to countries outside the EU. All the company's purchases come from businesses within the UK.

Hoddle Limited is registered for VAT and it makes both standard-rated and zero-rated supplies to its UK customers. All sales to other EU countries qualify as zero-rated. The company's local VAT office is at Bredon House, 14 Abbey Street, Pexley PY2 3WR.

Kelly Limited is separately registered for VAT; there is no group registration in force. Both companies have an accounting year ending on 31 March. There are no other companies in the Kelly group.

Hoddle Limited is a relatively small company and sometimes suffers from shortage of capacity to complete customers' jobs. In these cases, the printing work is done by Kelly Limited. Kelly then sells the completed products to Hoddle for onward sale to the customer. The sale from Kelly to Hoddle is recorded in the books of each company at cost; Kelly does not charge a profit margin.

In this simulation you are concerned with the accounting year ended 31 March 2004.

- To begin with you will be required to prepare the VAT return for Hoddle Limited in respect of the quarter ended 31 March 2004.

- You will then be required to prepare certain reports, both for internal use and for an external interfirm comparison scheme, covering the whole accounting year ended 31 March 2004. These reports will treat the two companies as a single group; they will contain consolidated figures, not figures for either of the two companies separately.

Today's date is 9 April 2004.

THE TASKS TO BE COMPLETED

1   Refer to the documents on pages 208 and 209; these have been received from Hoddle Ltd's suppliers during March 2004. No entries have yet been made in Hoddle Ltd's books of account in respect of these documents. You are required to explain how you will deal with them when preparing Hoddle Ltd's VAT return for the period January to March 2004. Use the blank page 210.

2   Refer to the sales day book summary, purchases day book summary, cash book summary and petty cash book summary on pages 211 and 212. These have been printed out from Hoddle Ltd's computerised accounting system for the period January to March 2004. (You are reminded that these summaries do not include the documents dealt with in Task 1.) Refer also to the memo on page 213. Using this information you are required to complete the VAT return of Hoddle Limited for the quarter ended 31 March 2004. A blank VAT return is provided on page 214.

3   The Group Accountant is considering adoption of the cash accounting scheme for VAT. He believes that Hoddle Limited (though not Kelly Limited) might qualify for the scheme. He has asked you to draft a letter to the VAT office, in his name, requesting certain details of the scheme. He is interested in the turnover limit for the scheme, particularly since Hoddle is a member of a group of companies, and he wants to know how the scheme affects a company in its dealings with bad debts. You are required to draft this letter using the blank letterhead on page 215.

4   Refer to the profit and loss account of Kelly Limited on page 216, which covers the period 1 January to 31 March 2004. You are required to prepare a profit and loss account for the same period in which the results of Hoddle and Kelly are consolidated. Enter your answer on the form provided on page 217, as follows:

   •   Enter the results of Kelly Ltd in the first column of the form.

   •   Using the information already provided for earlier tasks construct the results of Hoddle Ltd and enter them in the second column. Note that Hoddle Ltd's stock at 1 January 2004 was valued at £14,638, while stock at 31 March 2004 was valued at £16,052.

   •   Make the appropriate adjustments in the third column to eliminate the effects of trading between Kelly Ltd and Hoddle Ltd.

   •   Calculate the consolidated figures and enter them in the fourth column.

5   Refer to the information on pages 218 to 220. Using this, and information already provided for earlier tasks, you are required to prepare a report for the Accountant on the group results for the year ended 31 March 2004. Your report should contain the following:

   •   Key ratios: gross profit margin; net profit margin; return on shareholders' capital employed.

   •   Sales revenue for each quarter; both in actual terms and indexed to a common base.

   •   A pie chart showing the proportion of annual (unindexed) sales earned in each quarter.

   Use your own stationery to set out your answer. Note that you are not required to comment on the results for the year, merely to present them according to the instructions above.

6   You are required to complete the interfirm comparison form on page 221.

7   You are required to prepare a memo to the Group Accountant enclosing the interfirm comparison form for authorisation before despatch. Use the stationery on page 222.

Engineering Supplies Limited

Haddlefield Road, Blaysley CG6 6AW
Tel/fax: 01376 44531

Hoddle Limited
22 Formguard Street
Pexley
PY6 3QW

SALES INVOICE NO: *2155*

Date: *27 March 2004*

£

VAT omitted in error from invoice no 2139

£2,667.30 @ 17.5%   466.77

Total due   466.77

Terms: net 30 days

VAT registration: 318 1827 58

VAT INVOICE
ONLY

Alpha Stationery

Ainsdale Centre, Mexton EV1 4DF
Telephone 01392 43215

26 March 2004

1 box transparent folders: red

Total incl VAT @17.5%	14.84
Amount tendered	20.00
Change	5.16

VAT registration: 356 7612 33

JAMIESON & CO

Jamieson House, Baines Road, Gresham GM7 2PQ
Telephone: 01677 35567   Fax: 01677 57640

PROFORMA SALES INVOICE

VAT registration: *412 7553 67*

Hoddle Limited
22 Formguard Street
Pexley
PY6 3QW

	£
For professional services in connection with debt collection	
Our fees	350.00
VAT	61.25
Total due	411.25

A VAT invoice will be submitted when the total due is paid in full.

answers to Task 1

HODDLE LIMITED: SALES DAY BOOK SUMMARY
JANUARY TO MARCH 2004

	JAN £	FEB £	MAR £	TOTAL £
UK: ZERO RATED	20,091.12	22,397.00	23,018.55	65,506.67
UK: STANDARD-RATED - 17.5%	15,682.30	12,914.03	15,632.98	44,229.31
OTHER EU = ZERO RATED	874.12	4,992.66	5,003.82	10,870.60
VAT	2,744.40	2,259.95	2,735.77	7,740.12
TOTAL	39,391.94	42,563.64	46,391.12	128,346.70

(handwritten notes: 15,682.30 × 17.5% = 2,744.40)

HODDLE LIMITED: PURCHASES DAY BOOK SUMMARY
JANUARY TO MARCH 2004

	JAN £	FEB £	MAR £	TOTAL £
PURCHASES	14,532.11	20,914.33	15,461.77	50,908.21*
DISTRIBUTION EXPENSES	4,229.04	3,761.20	5,221.43	13,211.67
ADMIN EXPENSES	5,123.08	2,871.45	3,681.62	11,676.15
OTHER EXPENSES	1,231.00	1,154.99	997.65	3,383.64
VAT	4,027.97	4,543.22	4,119.34	12,690.53
TOTAL	29,143.20	33,245.19	29,481.81	91,870.20

*This figure includes £18,271 of purchases from Kelly Limited.

HODDLE LIMITED: CASH BOOK SUMMARY
JANUARY TO MARCH 2004

	JAN £	FEB £	MAR £	TOTAL £
PAYMENTS				
TO CREDITORS	12,901.37	15,312.70	18,712.44	46,926.51
TO PETTY CASH	601.40	555.08	623.81	1,780.29
WAGES/SALARIES	5,882.18	6,017.98	66,114.31	18,014.47
TOTAL	19,384.95	21,885.76	25,450.56	66,721.27
RECEIPTS				
VAT FROM CUSTOMS & EXCISE	2,998.01			2,998.01
FROM CUSTOMERS	29,312.44	34,216.08	36,108.77	99,637.29
TOTAL	32,310.45	34,216.08	36,108.77	102,635.30
SURPLUS FOR MONTH	12,925.50	12,330.32	10,658.21	
BALANCE B/F	-8,712.41	4,213.09	16,543.41	
BALANCE C/F	4,213.09	16,543.41	27,201.62	

HODDLE LIMITED: PETTY CASH BOOK SUMMARY
JANUARY TO MARCH 2004

	JAN £	FEB £	MAR £	TOTAL £
PAYMENTS				
STATIONERY	213.85	80.12	237.58	531.55
TRAVEL	87.34	76.50	102.70	266.54
OFFICE EXPENSES	213.66	324.08	199.51	737.25
VAT	86.55	74.38	84.02	244.95
TOTAL	601.40	555.08	623.81	1,780.29
RECEIPTS				
FROM CASH BOOK	601.40	555.08	623.81	1,780.29
SURPLUS FOR MONTH	0.00	0.00	0.00	
BALANCE B/F	200.00	200.00	200.00	
BALANCES C/F	200.00	200.00	200.00	

MEMORANDUM

To: Sol Bellcamp

From: Sherry Teddingham

Date: 6 April 2004

Subject: Bad Debt – Batty Limited

As you probably know, we have had great difficulty in persuading the above customer to pay what he owes us. We invoiced him in July 2003 (on 30 days terms) for £420 plus VAT at the standard rate, but he has always disputed the debt and it looks as though we will never recover it. We wrote it off to the bad debt account in March of this year, so you should take this into account when preparing the VAT return for the quarter just ended.

420 × 17.5% = 73.50 B.D. – VAT

SPECIMEN

Value Added Tax Return

For the period
01 01 04 to 31 03 04

For Official Use

HM Customs
and Excise

081 578 4060 19 100 03 98   Q35192
MR SHERRY TEDDINGHAM
HODDLE LIMITED
22 FORMGUARD STREET
PEXLEY
PY6 3QW   219921/10

Your VAT Office telephone number is 01682 386000

Registration Number	Period
578 4060 19	03 04

You could be liable to a financial penalty if your completed return and all the VAT payable are not received by the due date.

Due date: 30 04 04

For Official Use

Before you fill in this form please read the notes on the back and the VAT leaflet *"Filling in your VAT return"*. Fill in all boxes clearly in ink, and write 'none' where necessary. Don't put a dash or leave any box blank. If there are no pence write "00" in the pence column. Do not enter more than one amount in any box.

For official use

		£	p
VAT due in this period on **sales** and other outputs	1		
VAT due in this period on **acquisitions** from other **EC Member States**	2		
Total VAT due **(the sum of boxes 1 and 2)**	3		
VAT reclaimed in this period on **purchases** and other inputs (including acquisitions from the EC)	4		
Net VAT to be paid to Customs or reclaimed by you **(Difference between boxes 3 and 4)**	5		
Total value of **sales** and all other outputs excluding any VAT. **Include your box 8 figure**	6		00
Total value of **purchases** and all other inputs excluding any VAT. **Include your box 9 figure**	7		00
Total value of all **supplies** of goods and related services, excluding any VAT, to other **EC Member States**	8		00
Total value of all **acquisitions** of goods and related services, excluding any VAT, from other **EC Member States**	9		00

Retail schemes. If you have used any of the schemes in the period covered by this return, enter the relevant letter(s) in this box.

If you are enclosing a payment please tick this box.

DECLARATION: You, or someone on your behalf, must sign below.

I, ...declare that the
(Full name of signatory in BLOCK LETTERS)

information given above is true and complete.

Signature ....Date ....19.............

A false declaration can result in prosecution.

B

0196929   PCU(November 1995)

VAT 100 (Half)

HODDLE LIMITED

22 Formguard Street
Pexley
PY6 3QW

Tel 01682 431256 Fax 01682 431874 E-mail Glyn@Hoddle.amtrex.com
VAT Reg 578 4060 19

Registered Office: 22 Formguard Street, Pexley, PY6 3QW. Registered in England No 2314561

KELLY LIMITED
PROFIT AND LOSS ACCOUNT
FOR THE THREE MONTHS ENDED 31 MARCH 2004

	£	£
Sales to external customers		275,601
Sales to Hoddle Limited at cost		20,167*
Total sales		295,768
Opening Stock	28,341	
Purchases	136,095	
	164,436	
Closing Stock	31,207	
Cost of sales		133,229
Gross profit		162,539
Wages and salaries	47,918	
Distribution expenses	28,341	
Administration expenses	30,189	
Stationery	2,541	
Travel	2,001	
Office expenses	3,908	
Interest payable	12,017	
Other expenses	11,765	
		138,680
Net profit for the period		23,859

*This figure includes £1,896 in respect of a job completed on 31 March 2004 but not delivered to Hoddle Limited until 1 April 2004. It is not included in Hoddle Ltd's purchases for the period ended 31 March.

KELLY LTD AND HODDLE LTD CONSOLIDATED PROFIT AND LOSS ACCOUNT

FOR THE THREE MONTHS ENDED 31 MARCH 2004

	Kelly £	Hoddle £	Adjustments £	Consolidated £
Sales				
Opening stock				
Purchases				
Closing stock				
Cost of sales				
Gross profit				
Wages and salaries				
Distribution expenses				
Administration expenses				
Stationery				
Travel				
Office expenses				
Interest payable				
Other expenses				
TOTAL				
Net profit for the period				

KELLY LTD AND HODDLE LTD
CONSOLIDATED BALANCE SHEET AT 31 MARCH 2004

	£	£	£
Fixed assets at net book value			1,229,348
Current assets			
Stock		49,155	
Trade debtors		223,009	
VAT recoverable		13,451	
Cash at bank and in hand		40,088	
		325,703	
Current liabilities			
Trade creditors	136,531		
Other creditors	11,740		
		148,271	
Net current assets			177,432
			1,406,780
Long-term liability			
Loan repayable in 2004			(372,072)
			1,034,708
FINANCED BY			
Capital and reserves			
Called up share capital			234,167
Retained profits			800,541
			1,034,708

KELLY LTD AND HODDLE LTD: QUARTERLY CONSOLIDATED PROFIT AND LOSS ACCOUNTS FOR THE YEAR ENDED 31 MARCH 2004

	1 Apr 2003- 30 Jun 2003 £	1 Jul 2003- 30 Sep 2003 £	1 Oct 2003- 31 Dec 2003 £	1 Jan 2004- 31 Mar 2004 £	1 Apr 2003- 31 Mar 2004 £
Sales	325,719	275,230	306,321		
Cost of sales	134,861	109,421	121,358		
Gross profit	190,858	165,809	184,963		
Wages and salaries	63,314	61,167	64,412		
Distribution expenses	34,217	30,135	31,221		
Administration expenses	34,765	33,012	36,415		
Stationery	2,981	2,671	3,008		
Travel	1,975	1,876	2,413		
Office expenses	4,412	4,713	3,083		
Interest payable	12,913	12,714	12,432		
Other expenses	10,981	16,421	15,431		
	165,558	162,709	168,415		
Net profit for the period	25,300	3,100	16,548		

Note to students: complete the above schedule by filling in the figures for the final quarter in the fourth column and totalling the figures for the year in the fifth column.

MEMORANDUM

To: Sol Bellcamp

From: Sherry Teddingham

Subject: Adjusting for the effects of price rises

Date: 2 April 2004

When presenting your quarterly reports on group results please include an item of information additional to that which you normally present. As well as noting sales revenue by quarter, please present quarterly sales revenue adjusted to take account of price rises.

I have identified a suitable index as follows:

First quarter 2002/03 (base period)	231.8
First quarter 2003/04	239.3
Second quarter 2003/04	241.5
Third quarter 2003/04	244.0
Fourth quarter 2003/04	241.8

I will keep you informed of future movements in this index.

INTERFIRM COMPARISON DATA

Name of company ....

Year ended   ....

DATA	£	% of sales	Industry best	Industry average
Sales				
Gross Profit			62.1%	57.3%
Net Profit			10.4%	5.8%
Fixed Assets				
Current assets				
Current Liabilities				
Return on Capital Employed			10.3%	9.0%

NOTES ON COMPLETION OF FORM

- Enter figures in the blank white boxes.

- 'Sales' means sales to external customers. Inter-company, inter-divisional or inter-branch sales should be excluded.

- Fixed assets should be stated at net book value.

- Return on capital employed is net profit before interest charges, divided by the total of fixed assets (stated at net book value) and net current assets.

MEMORANDUM

To:

From:

Date:

Subject:

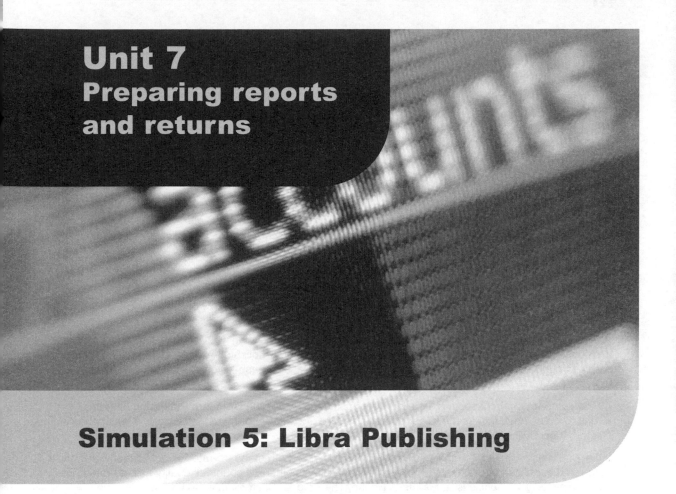

Unit 7
Preparing reports and returns

Simulation 5: Libra Publishing

NVQ Element coverage

7.1   prepare and present periodic performance reports

7.2   prepare reports and returns for outside agencies

7.3   prepare VAT returns

Scenario and contents

This simulation is based on Libra Publishing, a company which publishes educational books and computer software. The tasks include:

■   preparation of a VAT Return from the accounting records

■   dealing with queries involving VAT

■   consolidating the profit and loss accounts for the two operating divisions: Libra Books and Libra Software

■   preparing an internal report presenting key ratios from financial statements

■   preparation of an external financial report to a lending bank

Suggested time allocation: three hours plus fifteen minutes reading time

SIMULATION 5
LIBRA PUBLISHING

THE SITUATION

Your name is Thomas Handy. You work as an Accounting Technician for a publishing company, Libra Publishing Limited. You report to the Finance Director, William Collins.

Libra Publishing produces educational books which it distributes to colleges and schools throughout the UK. It has also diversified into producing CD ROMs and software which it sells into the educational market. Most of its customers are UK-based educational establishments, but sales are also made to English schools and colleges in the EU.

At the beginning of the financial year (1 July 2003) Libra Publishing was divided into two operating divisions: Libra Books and Libra Software. During the year Libra Publishing expanded its mail order sales, partly through its website. This resulted in a large increase in cash sales, particularly of educational software.

All the company's purchases are supplied from businesses within the UK. Libra Publishing operates from a unit on an industrial estate. The address is Unit 12 Oldwood Industrial Estate, Melbury Road, Casterbridge CB2 3GH.

Libra Publishing Limited is registered for VAT and it makes both standard-rated supplies (software) and zero-rated supplies (books) to its UK customers. All sales to other EU countries qualify as zero-rated. The company's local VAT office is at Mellstock House, The Parade, Casterbridge CB1 4TH.

In this simulation you are concerned with the accounting year ended 30 June 2004.

There are two series of tasks in this simulation:

1   The preparation of data for the VAT Return for Libra Publishing Limited (incorporating both publishing divisions) for the VAT quarter ending 30 June 2004.

2   The preparation of data for reports due at the end of the financial year: an internal financial report consolidating the figures for the two operating divisions and an external report of financial data for Centro Bank Plc from which Libra Publishing is borrowing £60,000.

The date is 5 July 2004.

During the course of the week a new trainee, Kerry Gold, will be working with you to learn the procedures and gain experience of the queries and problems that inevitably arise from time-to-time.

THE TASKS TO BE COMPLETED

1   Bella Donn, the Marketing Director of Libra Software has just produced an educational package which includes a textbook and a CD ROM disk which are film-wrapped together. The planned launch date is 1 August. Normally books are zero-rated for VAT and CDs are standard-rated. She asks you as the office VAT expert: "Is VAT chargeable on the whole pack, or just part of it?" You telephone the local VAT office to find out and they ask you to send in a sample of the package so that they can assess the VAT liability. You are to draft a letter (which will accompany the sample package) to the VAT Office on the letterhead shown on page 226. The address to write to is HM Customs & Excise, Mellstock House, The Parade, Casterbridge CB1 4TH. The person you spoke to on the telephone at the VAT Office on 2 July was Miss Annie Day. The letter should be prepared for the signature of Damon Wildene, Accounts Manager.

2   A computer printout of bad debts written off and put through Bad Debts Written Off Account is handed to you (see page 227). The list is headed "Information – for the VAT return". List and total on page 227 the bad debts you will claim relief for in the VAT return for the quarter ending 30 June 2004. Note that all goods are despatched within two working days of the invoice date.

3   On page 228 there are a number of summaries for the last VAT quarter, which need completing:
   *   the sales day book summary (already adjusted for bad debts written off)
   *   purchases day book summary
   *   cash book and petty cash book summaries

   On page 229 there is a schedule of further data collected for the VAT return.

   The figures are for both operating divisions of Libra Publishing – they have been consolidated.

   Using this information you are required to draw up a VAT Control Account for Libra Publishing for the VAT quarter ending 30 June 2004. Use the VAT Control Account set out on page 229.

4   With the data you now have compiled, you are to complete the VAT return of Libra Publishing Limited for the quarter ended 30 June 2004. A blank VAT 100 is provided on page 230. The form should be prepared for the signature of William Collins and left undated.

5   Kerry (the trainee) asks "When has the form got to be sent off? What would happen if someone forgot to send it off by the due date?" Write down on page 231 your reply to these two questions.

6   The schedule on page 232 sets out the profit and loss figures for Libra Books and Libra Software for the financial year to 30 June 2004. You are required to calculate the profit and loss results for the two divisions, and then consolidate the results. You must adjust for the internal sale by Libra Books of computer manuals to Libra Software at an internal transfer price of £25,000. The columns on page 232 are for the two sets of divisional figures (columns 1 & 2), the adjustments for the internal transfer (column 3) and the consolidated results (column 4). Assume that all the transferred stock of computer manuals has been sold.

7   A draft balance sheet for Libra Publishing Limited is shown on page 233. Using this, and the consolidated profit and loss account (page 232), you are required to complete a schedule (page 234) comparing the company's key ratios and performance indicators for 2003 and 2004.

8   Using the completed schedule on page 234, draw up a compound bar chart showing the sales, gross profit and net profit for the two years. Use the graph paper on page 235 or a spreadsheet.

9   Libra Publishing has a £60,000 long-term bank loan from Centro Bank Plc. As part of the terms of the loan it has to send in regular reports of its current assets and current liabilities figures. These provide the bank with an indication of the company's ability to repay the loan. The more funds the company has available in its hands, or due in the short term, the more able it is to repay the loan. Complete the pro-forma return to Centro Bank (page 236) with data from the balance sheet.

Libra Publishing

Unit 12 Oldwood Industrial Estate, Melbury Road, Casterbridge CB2 3GH

Tel 01603 289424 Fax 01603 289777 E-mail books@libra.u-mail.com
VAT Reg GB 5463 7652 65

Libra Publishing Limited, Registered in England No 0344748

Information – for the VAT Return – all posted to Bad Debts A/c

BAD DEBTS WRITTEN OFF 30 JUNE 2004

invoice date	invoice due	debtor	net amount (£)	VAT amount (£)
30.08.03	30.09.03	Verey Computers	400.00	70.00
16.09.03	31.10.03	Holbein Bookshop	678.90	nil
19.10.03	31.11.03	Bacon Books	567.95	nil
05.11.03	05.12.03	ComputaVision	66.75	11.68
12.12.03	31.12.03	CD Supplies Ltd	341.00	59.67
15.12.03	15.01.04	Roman Software	672.50	117.68
07.01.04	28.02.04	Bretherton Books	562.50	nil
12.03.04	30.04.04	Iris School Supplies	450.00	78.75
01.04.04	30.04.04	Bitstream Ltd	256.00	44.80

VAT – BAD DEBT RELIEF LISTING

VAT Return for quarter April - June 2004

invoice date	invoice due	debtor	net amount (£)	VAT amount (£)
TOTAL				£

LIBRA PUBLISHING: SALES DAY BOOK SUMMARY
01 April to 30 June 2004

	April	May	June	TOTAL
	£	£	£	£
UK Zero-rated	70,654.34	65,723.90	69,674.11	
UK standard-rated	5,678.90	7,845.12	6,982.56	
EU sales (non-UK)	453.78	1,117.60	231.90	
VAT	993.80	1,372.89	1,221.94	

LIBRA PUBLISHING: PURCHASES DAY BOOK SUMMARY
01 April to 30 June 2004

	April	May	June	TOTAL
	£	£	£	£
Purchases/Expenses	45,786.25	36,567.80	50,786.12	
VAT	2,675.78	1,856.60	3,456.60	

LIBRA PUBLISHING: CASH BOOK SUMMARY – NON CREDIT ITEMS
01 April to 30 June 2004

	April	May	June	TOTAL
	£	£	£	£
PAYMENTS				
Cash Purchases	1,341.75	3,890.00	2,873.45	
VAT	234.80	680.75	502.85	
RECEIPTS				
Cash Sales	12,360.00	7,930.88	11,703.67	
VAT	1,348.90	983.40	1,156.75	

LIBRA PUBLISHING:PETTY CASH BOOK SUMMARY
01 April to 30 June 2004

	April	May	June	TOTAL
	£	£	£	£
Purchases/Expenses	239.90	198.75	310.70	
VAT	28.70	23.76	35.20	

Libra Publishing: VAT 100 data

VAT quarter 04–06/04

Sales Credit Notes	Net £2,560.00, VAT £245.00
Suppliers' Credit Notes	Net £1,260.00, VAT £145.50
Previous periods' errors	VAT underpaid 09–12/03 £60.60
EU Acquisitions	None
Other notes	None

VAT Control Account: Libra Publishing

VAT deductible: input tax	£	VAT payable: output tax	£
Purchases Day Book		Sales Day Book	
less credit notes		*less* credit notes	
Cash Book		Cash Book	
Petty Cash Book			
EU Acquisitions		EU Acquisitions	
Correction of error		Correction of error	
Bad debt relief			
TOTAL INPUT TAX		TOTAL OUTPUT TAX	
		less TOTAL INPUT TAX	
		equals VAT DUE	

SPECIMEN

Value Added Tax Return

For the period
01 04 04 to 30 06 04

For Official Use

HM Customs
and Excise

625 454 7108 51 100 03 99 Q25147

LIBRA PUBLISHING LIMITED
UNIT 12 OLDWOOD INDUSTRIAL ESTATE
MELBURY ROAD
CASTERBRIDGE
CB2 3GH

Registration Number	Period
5463 7652 65	06 04

You could be liable to a financial penalty if your completed return and all the VAT payable are not received by the due date.

Due date: **31 07 04**

For
Official
Use

Before you fill in this form please read the notes on the back and the VAT leaflet *"Filling in your VAT return"*. Fill in all boxes clearly in ink, and write 'none' where necessary. Don't put a dash or leave any box blank. If there are no pence write "00" in the pence column. Do not enter more than one amount in any box.

For official use			£	p
	VAT due in this period on **sales** and other outputs	1		
	VAT due in this period on **acquisitions** from other **EC Member States**	2		
	Total VAT due **(the sum of boxes 1 and 2)**	3		
	VAT reclaimed in this period on **purchases** and other inputs (including acquisitions from the EC)	4		
	Net VAT to be paid to Customs or reclaimed by you **(Difference between boxes 3 and 4)**	5		
	Total value of **sales** and all other outputs excluding any VAT. **Include your box 8 figure**	6		00
	Total value of **purchases** and all other inputs excluding any VAT. **Include your box 9 figure**	7		00
	Total value of all **supplies** of goods and related services, excluding any VAT, to other **EC Member States**	8		00
	Total value of all **acquisitions** of goods and related services, excluding any VAT, from other **EC Member States**	9		00

Retail schemes. If you have used any of the schemes in the period covered by this return, enter the relevant letter(s) in this box.

If you are enclosing a payment please tick this box.

DECLARATION: You, or someone on your behalf, must sign below.

I, ...declare that the
      (Full name of signatory in BLOCK LETTERS)

information given above is true and complete.

Signature ....Date ....19...............

A false declaration can result in prosecution.

B

0196929   PCU(November 1995)

VAT 100 (Half)

answers to Kerry's questions

LIBRA PUBLISHING LIMITED
PROFIT AND LOSS ACCOUNT FOR THE YEAR ENDED 30 JUNE 2004

	BOOKS DIVISION £	SOFTWARE DIVISION £	ADJUSTMENTS £	CONSOLIDATED FIGURES £
Sales	856,050	155,900		
Opening stock	75,800	56,890		
Purchases	565,300	75,900		
Closing stock	79,585	67,812		
Cost of sales				
Gross profit				
Wages and salaries	101,856	35,670		
Distribution expenses	25,678	5,671		
Administration expenses	3,475	1,205		
Marketing	5,786	4,675		
R&D	2,500	4,700		
Royalties	65,561	10,652		
Interest payable	2,563	456		
Other expenses	267	571		
TOTAL				
Net profit for the period				

LIBRA PUBLISHING LIMITED
BALANCE SHEET AS AT 30 JUNE 2004

	£	£	£
Fixed assets at net book value			1,521,700
Current assets			
Stock		147,397	
Trade debtors		176,493	
VAT		2,598	
Bank		45,600	
		372,088	
Current liabilities			
Trade creditors	259,671		
Royalties due	35,600		
Other creditors	12,362		
		307,633	
Net current assets			64,455
Long-term bank loan			(60,000)
			1,526,155
FINANCED BY			
Capital and reserves			
Called up share capital			1,000,000
Profit and loss			526,155
			1,526,155

LIBRA PUBLISHING LIMITED

COMPARATIVE KEY FIGURES AND RATIOS

FINANCIAL YEARS ENDED 30 JUNE 2003 & 2004

	2003	2004	% change (+ or −)
Sales	£859,625		
Gross Profit	£315,870		
Gross Profit Ratio	37%		
Net Profit	£101,120		
Net Profit Ratio	12%		
Capital & Reserves	£1,411,984		
Return on Capital Employed*	7%		

Notes

*Formula: Return on Capital Employed =

$$\frac{\text{net profit}}{\text{capital and reserves}} \times 100$$

Calculate percentages to the
nearest percentage point.

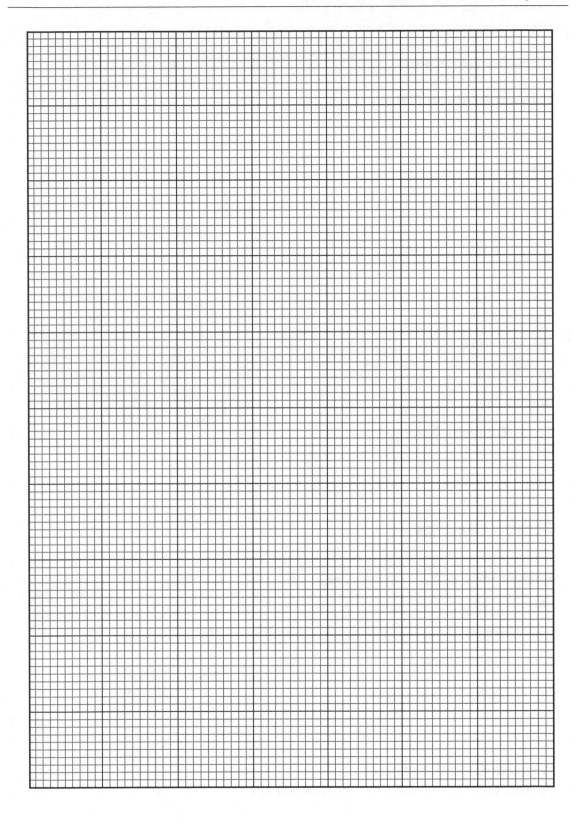

CENTRO BANK PLC

Current Position Return

Business Name ....

Date ....

CURRENT ASSETS

£

Stock Held

Trade Debtors

VAT reclaimable

Bank Balance

Other

TOTAL CURRENT ASSETS £ _____ 1

CURRENT LIABILITIES

£

Trade Creditors

VAT due

Bank Overdraft

Other amounts payable

TOTAL CURRENT LIABILITIES £ _____ 2

WORKING CAPITAL SURPLUS
(CURRENT ASSETS LESS CURRENT LIABILITIES) £ _____ 1–2

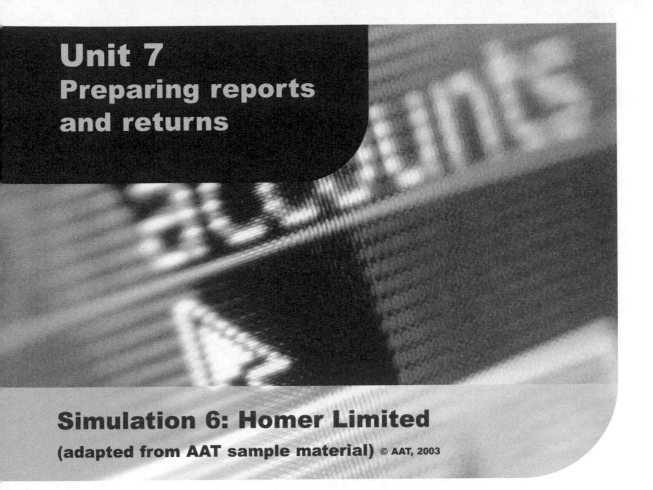

Unit 7
Preparing reports and returns

Simulation 6: Homer Limited
(adapted from AAT sample material) © AAT, 2003

NVQ Element coverage

7.1 prepare and present periodic performance reports

7.2 prepare reports and returns for outside agencies

7.3 prepare VAT returns

Scenario and contents

This simulation is based on Homer Limited, a manufacturer of 'Barts'. The tasks in the simulation involve:

- consolidation and presentation in graphical form of sales figures from the company's two divisions

- adjustment of the sales figures to an industrial index

- completion of a bank loan application form

- analysis of performance indicators

- completion of a VAT Return and dealings with the VAT Office

Suggested time allocation: three hours plus fifteen minutes reading time

SIMULATION 6
HOMER LIMITED

SITUATION

Your name is Amir Pindhi and you work as an Accounts Assistant for Homer Limited, Springfield Drive, Pantile Trading Estate, Coventry, CV32 1AW.

Homer Limited is a manufacturing company, producing a single product, the 'Bart'. The company's year end is 31 March.

Today's date is Monday 14 April 2003.

DIVISIONAL STRUCTURE OF HOMER LIMITED

All production activities are carried out in the Manufacturing division. This division transfers most of its output to the Sales Division, which sells the output to external customers.

The Manufacturing Division transfers finished output to the Sales division at full production cost, but without any mark-up for profit. The Manufacturing division also sells some of its finished output direct to external customers.

ACCOUNTING FOR VAT

Homer Limited is registered for VAT.

Sales of Barts to UK customers are subject to VAT at the standard rate of 17.5%.

The company also exports to other countries within the European Union (EU). Such exports qualify as zero-rated. The company does not export to countries outside the EU. The company does not import any goods or services.

The local VAT office for Homer Limited is at Bell House, 33 Lambert Road, Coventry, CV12 8TR.

APPLICATION FOR BANK LOAN

The company is about to seek a long-term loan from its bankers to finance expansion plans. The bank has requested some financial information in support of this application, and one of your responsibilities will be to present this information in the form required by the bank.

PRESENTING YOUR WORK

Unless you are told otherwise:

- all ratios and statistics should be computed and presented to two decimal places

- monetary amounts should be computed and presented to the nearest penny

TASKS

1   Refer to the table on page 240 which analyses monthly sales achieved by each of the company's two divisions during the years ended 31 March 2002 and 31 March 2003.

Consolidate these figures to arrive at the monthly sales and cumulative sales for each month in the two year period. Note that this task relates only to sales made to external customers, not to transfers within the company from the Manufacturing division to the Sales division. You should set out your answer on the schedule on page 243.

2   Using the figures calculated in Task 1, plot a line graph on page 244. The graph should show the cumulative sales achieved month by month during the year ended 31 March 2002 and, as a separate line, the cumulative sales achieved month by month during the year ended 31 March 2003. As in Task 1, you are concerned only with the sales to external customers, not with internal transfers from Manufacturing to Sales.

3   On page 241 you will find month-by-month values of an index appropriate to the industry in which Homer operates (the Dowe index). The values given are stated by reference to a base figure of 100, which was the value of the index in the base period January 1998.

Calculate the indexed value of the monthly sales to external customers, in March 2003 terms, for each month's sales in the year ended 31 March 2003. Your answer should be set out on page 245 in accordance with the notes on that page.

4   Refer to the information on page 241.

Complete the extract from the loan application form on page 246.

Write a memo to the Accountant, Sonia Liesl, enclosing the form for her attention and approval prior to its submission to the bank. Use a blank memo form on page 247 and date your memo 14 April 2003.

5   Write a memo to Sonia Liesl, presenting the following statistics for her information, and very briefly suggesting a possible reason for the movement in each statistic's value since year ended 31 March 2002. (The 2002 values are given in brackets below).

• The gross profit percentage for year ended 31 March 2003. (The percentage in year ended 31 March 2002 was 43.15%).

• The net profit percentage for year ended 31 March 2003 (2002: 7.84%).

• The production cost per 'Bart' produced and sold in year ended 31 March 2003 (2002: £10.83).

• The value of sales earned per employee in year ended 31 March 2003 (2002: £26,018.13).

Use a memo form on page 247 and date your memo 14 April 2003.

6   Refer to the information on page 242 that relates to the company's VAT return for the quarter ended on 31 March 2003.

Complete the blank return on page 248. Note that the return is to be signed by the Accountant, Sonia Liesl, and that payment of any balance due to Customs & Excise will be made by cheque.

7   Refer to the memo from Sonia Liesl on page 242.

Draft a letter to your local VAT office (in the name of Sonia Liesl) asking for the required information. Use the letterhead on page 249.

8   Reply to Sonia Liesl's memo giving her the brief details she requests, and enclosing the draft letter prepared in Task 7 above. Use the blank memo form on page 250.

DATA

Monthly sales during the years ended 31 March 2002 and 31 March 2003
All figures in £000. All figures exclude VAT.

| | Sales Division | Manufacturing Division | | |
	Total	*To external customers*	*To Sales Division*	*Total*
2001/2002				
April	350	34	185	219
May	225	46	128	174
June	190	32	96	128
July	255	54	138	192
August	310	36	166	202
September	238	24	148	172
October	220	20	125	145
November	295	34	172	206
December	240	39	182	221
January	257	20	150	170
February	230	14	155	169
March	340	45	218	263
2002/2003				
April	339	42	197	239
May	189	53	119	172
June	223	14	109	123
July	295	44	214	258
August	280	50	176	226
September	265	34	138	172
October	219	12	119	131
November	322	50	170	220
December	316	39	180	219
January	281	29	148	177
February	248	24	168	192
March	240	51	185	236

Dowe Industrial index: base = 100 (January 1998)

2002	April	123.8
	May	124.4
	June	124.9
	July	125.7
	August	126.3
	September	127.0
	October	127.5
	November	128.1
	December	128.9
2003	January	129.6
	February	130.2
	March	131.0

Statistical information relating to year ended 31 March 2003

Production cost of Barts produced and sold in the year	£2,190,000
Gross profit for the year	£1,470,000
Administration costs for the year	£580,000
Distribution costs for the year	£430,000
Total of all other costs for the year	£150,000
Net profit for the year before taxation	£310,000
Net profit for the previous year before taxation	£278,000
Total capital employed	£6,590,000
Number of Barts produced and sold in the year	199,000
Average number of employees in the year	143

The following details have been extracted from the company's day books.

All figures are exclusive of VAT.

SALES DAY BOOK TOTALS: QUARTER ENDED 31 MARCH 2003

	January	February	March	Total
	£	£	£	£
UK sales: standard rated	282,862.57	245,871.89	269,088.11	797,822.57
EC sales: zero-rated	27,143.05	26,126.66	21,920.34	75,190.05
Total	310,005.62	271,998.55	291,008.45	873,012.62
VAT on UK sales	49,500.95	43,027.58	47,090.42	139,618.95

PURCHASES DAY BOOK TOTALS: QUARTER ENDED 31 MARCH 2003

	January	February	March	Total
	£	£	£	£
Purchases/expenses	186,007.66	163,265.69	171,295.45	520,568.80
VAT on purchases/expenses	32,551.34	28,571.50	29,976.70	91,099.54

A debt of £658, inclusive of VAT, was written off as bad in March 2003.

The related sale was made in June 2002. Bad debt relief is now to be claimed.

MEMORANDUM

To: Amir Pindhi

From: Sonia Liesl

Subject: VAT on imports

Date: 11 April 2003

As you may know, we have been in discussions with a supplier based in the Far East. We are considering importing certain components in future for use in our manufacturing activities.

Please could you remind me very briefly of the VAT implications if we decide to proceed with this. Please also draft a letter to the VAT office, in my name, requesting relevant publications so that we can be sure we account for the VAT correctly.

Thanks for your help.

ANSWER PAGES

Task 1   **SALES TO EXTERNAL CUSTOMERS**
Manufacturing and Sales divisions combined

	Monthly totals £000	Cumulative total for the year £000
2001/2002		
April		
May		
June		
July		
August		
September		
October		
November		
December		
January		
February		
March		
2002/2003		
April		
May		
June		
July		
August		
September		
October		
November		
December		
January		
February		
March		

Notes

1   In the first column, enter the monthly total of external sales achieved by the two divisions.

2   In the second column, enter the cumulative total of external sales in the accounting year.

Task 2

Task 3

INDEXED SALES TO EXTERNAL CUSTOMERS

Manufacturing and Sales divisions combined

	Unadjusted totals £000	Index factor	Indexed totals £000
2002/2003			
April			
May			
June			
July			
August			
September			
October			
November			
December			
January			
February			
March			

Notes

1   In the first column, insert the monthly totals of external sales calculated in Task 1.

2   In the second column, insert the index factor required to convert to March 2003 values.

3   In the third column, calculate the monthly sales in March 2003 terms (to the nearest £1,000).

Task 4

LOAN APPLICATION (extract)

Name of applicant company _____

Latest year for which accounting information is available _____

Total sales revenue

In latest year for which accounts are available   £ _____

In previous year   £ _____

Percentage change (+/-)   _____

Net profit after all expenses, before taxation

In latest year for which accounts are available   £ _____

In previous year   £ _____

Percentage change (+/-)   _____

Gross profit margin (%)   _____

Net profit margin (%)   _____

Return on capital employed (%)   _____

Notes

1   In the case of a company with a divisional structure, all figures should refer to the results of the company as a whole, not to individual divisions within the company.

2   Unless otherwise stated, all questions relate to the latest year for which accounting information is available.

3   Figures should be actual historical values, with no indexing for inflation.

4   Return on capital employed is defined as net profit for the year before taxation, divided by total capital employed.

MEMO

To:

From:

Subject:

Date:

Task 5

MEMO

To:

From:

Subject:

Date:

Task 6

SPECIMEN

Value Added Tax Return

For the period

01 01 03 to 31 03 03

HM Customs
and Excise

For Official Use

HOMER LIMITED
SPRINGFIELD DRIVE
PANTILE TRADING ESTATE
COVENTRY
CV32 1AW

Registration Number	Period
625 7816 29	03 03

You could be liable to a financial penalty if your completed return and all the VAT payable are not received by the due date.

Due date: **30 04 03**

For Official Use

Before you fill in this form please read the notes on the back and the VAT leaflet *"Filling in your VAT return"*. Fill in all boxes clearly in ink, and write 'none' where necessary. Don't put a dash or leave any box blank. If there are no pence write "00" in the pence column. Do not enter more than one amount in any box.

For official use			£	p
	VAT due in this period on **sales** and other outputs	**1**		
	VAT due in this period on **acquisitions** from other **EC Member States**	**2**		
	Total VAT due **(the sum of boxes 1 and 2)**	**3**		
	VAT reclaimed in this period on **purchases** and other inputs (including acquisitions from the EC)	**4**		
	Net VAT to be paid to Customs or reclaimed by you **(Difference between boxes 3 and 4)**	**5**		
	Total value of **sales** and all other outputs excluding any VAT. **Include your box 8 figure**	**6**		00
	Total value of **purchases** and all other inputs excluding any VAT. **Include your box 9 figure**	**7**		00
	Total value of all **supplies** of goods and related services, excluding any VAT, to other **EC Member States**	**8**		00
	Total value of all **acquisitions** of goods and related services, excluding any VAT, from other **EC Member States**	**9**		00

Retail schemes. If you have used any of the schemes in the period covered by this return, enter the relevant letter(s) in this box.

If you are enclosing a payment please tick this box.

DECLARATION: You, or someone on your behalf, must sign below.

I, ...declare that the
(Full name of signatory in BLOCK LETTERS)

information given above is true and complete.

Signature ....Date ....19...............

A false declaration can result in prosecution.

B

0196929   PCU(November 1995)

VAT 100 (Half)

Task 7

HOMER LIMITED

**Springfield Drive, Pantile Trading Estate Coventry CV32 1AW
Telephone: 02467 881235**

**Registered office: Springfield Drive, Pantile Trading Estate CV32 1AW
Registered in England, number 2007814**

Task 8

MEMO

To:

From:

Subject:

Date:

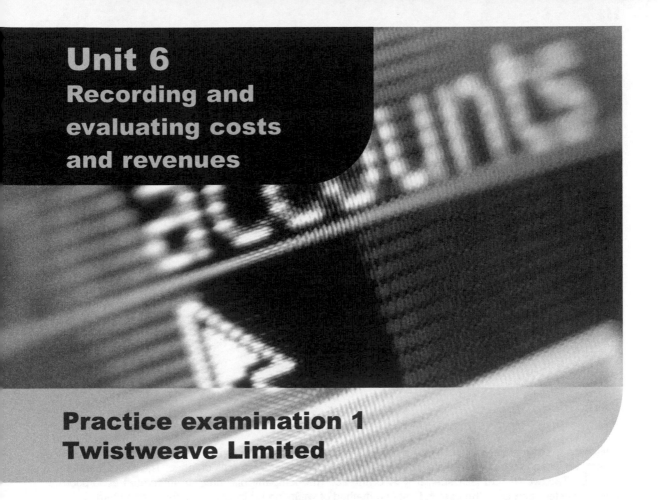

Unit 6
Recording and evaluating costs and revenues

Practice examination 1
Twistweave Limited

NVQ Element coverage

6.1   record and analyse information relating to direct costs and revenues

6.2   record and analyse information relating to the allocation, apportionment and absorption of overhead costs

6.3   prepare and evaluate estimates of costs and revenues

Suggested time allocation

Three hours and fifteen minutes (to include a recommended fifteen minutes reading time).

PRACTICE EXAMINATION 1
TWISTWEAVE LIMITED

This examination is in TWO sections.

You have to show competence in BOTH sections.

You should therefore attempt and aim to complete EVERY task in BOTH sections.

Blank space for workings is available on the pages, but all essential workings should be included within your answers, where appropriate.

You should spend about 90 minutes on each section.

Both sections are based on Twistweave Ltd.

DATA

Twistweave Ltd makes a single type of fabric, TW1, which is sold to other manufacturing companies, where it is used in various products. The output of TW1 is measured in rolls of fabric. The direct material used by Twistweave Ltd is a special type of thread. The company operates an integrated absorption costing system and uses the Last In First Out method of valuation for issues of material from stores.

You work as an accounting assistant at Twistweave Ltd and have been given the following tasks. Additional data is given as required for the tasks.

LIFO

SECTION 1

You should spend about 90 minutes on this section.

Tasks 1.1 and 1.2 relate to the budget for the next year. Tasks 1.3 to 1.6 relate to the month of March during the year to which the budget applies.

ADDITIONAL DATA

Twistweave Ltd has the following departments:

> Production
>
> Stores
>
> Administration
>
> Sales

The budgeted fixed overheads for the next year are:

	£
Indirect labour:	
Production	48,000
Stores	36,000
Administration	67,000
Sales	55,000
	206,000
Other administration overheads	45,000
Depreciation	120,000
Premises costs	80,000
Total fixed overheads	451,000

The following information is available:

Department:	Production	Stores	Administration	Sales
Net book value of fixed assets (£000s)	420	100	60	20 (60)
Percentage of floor area occupied	60%	20%	10%	10%

Fixed overheads are to be allocated and apportioned between departments using the most appropriate basis.

Task 1.1

Complete the table on the next page showing the allocation and apportionment of fixed overheads between the four departments.

Task 1.1 (continued)

Fixed overheads for the year	Basis	Total £	Production £	Stores £	Administration £	Sales £
Indirect labour	ALLOCATED	206,000	48,000	36,000	67,000	55,000
Other administration costs	ALLOCATED	45,000	—	—	45,000	—
Depreciation	NBV OF FIXED ASSETS	120,000	84,000	20,000	12,000	4,000
Premises costs	% OF FLOOR AREA	80,000	48,000	16,000	8,000	8,000
Budgeted fixed overheads		451,000	180,000	72,000	132,000	67,000

ADDITIONAL DATA

Production department fixed overheads are absorbed on the basis of budgeted direct labour hours.

72,000 hours of direct labour are budgeted for the next year.

Task 1.2

Calculate the budgeted fixed overhead absorption rate for the production department for the next year. (You will need to refer to your answer to Task 1.1.)

$$OAR = \frac{\text{Total Dept. Overheads}}{\text{Total Budgeted Hrs (Machine or Labour)}}$$

$$= \frac{£180,000}{72,000 \text{ hrs}} = £2.50 \text{ per hour}$$

ADDITIONAL DATA

Tasks 1.3 to 1.6 relate to the month of March during the year to which the budget applies. Production overheads are absorbed in March using the absorption rate calculated in Task 1.2 above.

Task 1.3

Twistweave Ltd uses the LIFO method for valuing issues of material to production and stocks of materials. Complete the stock card for thread shown on the next page. Use the boxes below the card to show your figures for stock issues if there is not room on the stock card itself.

STOCK CARD

Product: Thread (direct material)

Date	Receipts Quantity	Unit price £	Total cost £	Issues Quantity	Unit price £	Total £	Stock Quantity	Unit price £	Total £
1 Mar							1,900	50	95,000
5 Mar	500	52	26,000				500	52	26,000
10 Mar				800 *300 / 500*	*50 / 52*	*18,000 / 26,000*	*1,600*	*50*	*80,000*
12 Mar	1,000	52	52,000				*1,000*	*52*	*52,000*
17 Mar				800	*52*	*41,600*	*1,600 / 200*	*50 / 52*	*80,000 / 10,400*
19 Mar				300 *100 / 200*	*50 / 520*	*5,000 / 10,400*	*1,500*	*50*	*75,000*
23 Mar	1,000	53	53,000				*1,000*	*53*	*53,000*
24 Mar				1,100 *100 / 1000*	*50 / 53*	*5,000 / 53,000*	*1,400*	*50*	*70,000*
31 Mar c/d									

issue 10 Mar

issue 17 Mar

issue 19 Mar

issue 24 Mar

ADDITIONAL DATA

The following data relates to the direct labour for production of fabric TW1 for the month of March:

Direct labour hours worked	=	7,200 hours
Normal time hours	=	6,000 hours
Overtime hours	=	1,200 hours
Normal time rate per hour	=	£6.60
Overtime premium*	=	£3.30

*Total overtime premium is treated as an indirect cost.

Task 1.4

(a)   Complete the table below to record the book-keeping entries for direct wages and overtime premium for the month of March:

	Dr	Cr
Work in progress control account	• 6,000 × 6.6 = 39,600	
Production overhead control account	• 1,200 × 9.9 = 11,880	
Wages control account		. 51,480.

(b)   Referring to your answer to task 1.2, calculate the production overhead absorbed in the month of March.

$$7,200 \ hrs \ \times \ £2.50 \ = \ £18,000$$

Task 1.5

Refer to your answer to Task 1.3 to obtain the total value of direct material used in March. (There were no further issues of direct material in March.)

Referring also to your answers to Task 1.4, complete the table below to show:

(a)   the total cost of production of fabric TW1 in March

(b)   the unit cost of production of fabric TW1 in March

Product: TW1	Month: March	Output: 300 rolls
		£
Direct costs:		
Direct material (thread)		156,000 – all times
Direct labour		39,600
Production overheads absorbed		18,000
Total production cost		213,600
Unit cost of production (production cost per roll)		712.

Task 1.6

Referring to your answer to Task 1.4 (b), show the appropriate entries for production overhead absorbed and for over or under absorption in order to complete and balance the Production Overhead Control Account for March:

Production Overhead Control Account (for March)

Dr   Cr

	£		£
Wages control account	5,000	Work in Progress	14,000
Depreciation	7,000		
Premises costs	4,000		
Overabsorbed to P/L.	2,000		
as a profit			

SECTION 2

You should spend about 90 minutes on this section.

ADDITIONAL DATA

The managers of Twistweave Ltd are considering whether to develop a new fabric product, TW2, with different uses from those of TW1. The company would set up a separate department for TW2 and the new product would not affect sales of TW1. The data in this section all relates to the proposal to develop TW2 and is not connected to the tasks in Section 1.

Some forecasts of costs, sales, capital investment and future cash flows have been prepared for the new product.

Budgeted costs have been forecast for the first 6 months of production and sales of TW2, at two different volumes of output, as follows:

Product TW2: Production cost budget for first 6 months		
Output (rolls)	1,000	1,500
	£	£
Direct costs	200,000	300,000
Indirect labour	65,000	90,000
Depreciation	21,000	21,000
Premises costs	13,000	13,000
Total	299,000	424,000

Task 2.1

Identify the fixed, variable and semi-variable costs in the budget for TW2 and separate any semi-variable costs into their fixed and variable parts.

Indirect labour =

1,500	90,000	∴ 25,000
less 1,000	65,000	──── = £50
────	────	500 variable cost
500	25,000	per unit

∴ £50 × 1000 = £50,000

£65,000 –
– 50,000
£15,000 fixed

Task 2.2

Using your analysis in Task 2.1, complete the Production cost budget below for a volume of 1,200 rolls of TW2.

Product TW2: Production cost budget for first 6 months		
Output (rolls)		1,200
		£
Direct costs	1,200 × £200	240,000
Indirect labour	15,000 fixed 15,000 1,200 × 50 = + 60,000	75,000
Depreciation		21,000
Premises costs		13,000
Total		349,000

Task 2.3

Using your answers to Task 2.1, calculate the number of rolls of TW2 to be made and sold in the first 6 months in order to break even, assuming the budgeted selling price is £320 per roll.

320
$$-\frac{50 + 200}{70} = \text{Contrib/Unit}$$

Fixed Costs = 15,000
21,000
13,000
—
49,000

$$\frac{49,000}{70} = 700 \text{ Rolls} = \text{Break Even}$$

Task 2.4

Complete the table below to show the volume of production and sales of TW2 required in order to obtain a profit of £42,000 from this product in the first 6 months:

Total fixed costs	49,000
Required profit	42,000
Total contribution required	91,000
Contribution per unit	70
Volume required	1,300

ADDITIONAL DATA

Twistweave Ltd requires a payback period of less than 3 years and a rate of return of 12% per year on new projects. The following forecasts have been prepared, showing the relevant cash flows for TW2 over a five year period.

	Year 1 £000s	Year 2 £000s	Year 3 £000s	Year 4 £000s	Year 5 £000s
Initial investment	(300)				
Sales revenue		600	700	800	700
Relevant costs excluding depreciation		500	570	660	600
		100	130	140	100
12% present value factor	0.893	0.797	0.712	0.636	0.567

$$12\% = \frac{100}{112} \qquad \left(\frac{100}{112}\right)^2 \qquad \left(\frac{100}{112}\right)^4$$

Task 2.5

Calculate for the fabric TW2 project:

(a)   the payback period

| year | 1 | 2 | 3 | 4 | 5 |

Net cash Flow (000's)   (300)   (600-500) 100   (700-570) 130   (800-660) 140   (700-600) 100

Cumulative,   (300)   (200)   (70) ↑   70   170

Payback.

$$\frac{70}{140} = 0.5$$

∴ 3.5 years to payback.

(b)   the net present value (using the table below for your workings)

	Year 1 £000s	Year 2 £000s	Year 3 £000s	Year 4 £000s	Year 5 £000s
Net Cash flow	(300)	100	130	140	100.
12% present value factor	0.893	0.797	0.712	0.636	0.567
DCF	(267.90)	79.70	92.56	89.04	56.70

79.70 + 92.56 + 89.04 + 56.70

= 318

− 267.90

50,10 (000's)

Task 2.6

Referring to your answers to Task 2.5, write a short report on the proposed new fabric TW2 to the managers of Twistweave Ltd. Your report should include:

• a recommendation as to whether to proceed with the project

• brief comments on the disadvantages of each of the methods used

REPORT

To:

From:

Date:

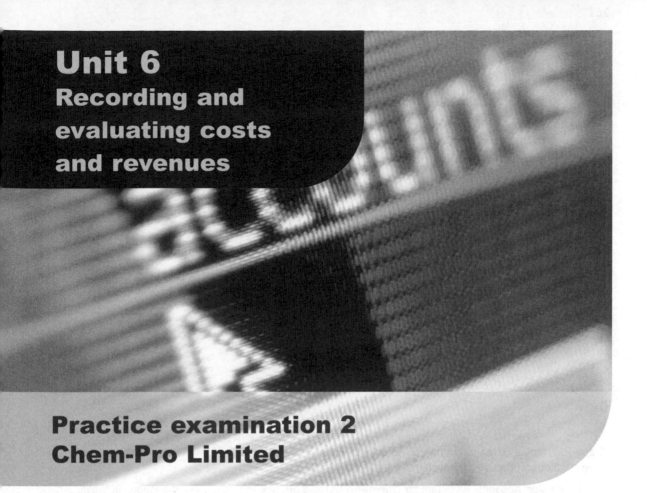

Unit 6
Recording and evaluating costs and revenues

Practice examination 2
Chem-Pro Limited

NVQ Element coverage

6.1 record and analyse information relating to direct costs and revenues

6.2 record and analyse information relating to the allocation, apportionment and absorption of overhead costs

6.3 prepare and evaluate estimates of costs and revenues

Suggested time allocation

Three hours and fifteen minutes (to include a recommended fifteen minutes reading time).

PRACTICE EXAMINATION 2
CHEM-PRO LIMITED

This examination is in TWO sections.

You have to show competence in BOTH sections.

You should therefore attempt and aim to complete EVERY task in BOTH sections.

Blank space for workings is available on these pages, but all essential workings should be included within your answers, where appropriate.

You should spend about 90 minutes on each section.

Both sections are based on Chem-Pro Ltd.

DATA

Chem-Pro Ltd is a manufacturer of chemicals used in the plastics industry. The company uses an integrated absorption costing system.

You work as an Accounts Assistant for Chem-Pro Ltd and are asked to carry out the following tasks.

SECTION 1

You should spend about 90 minutes on this section.

The tasks in this section all relate to the Processing Division of Chem-Pro Ltd for the month of July.

The direct material is a chemical, XR, measured in litres. Process costing is used in the Processing Division. The output of the Processing Division is Chem-Base, which is measured in litres. Further data will be given where required for the tasks.

The direct material XR is issued to the production process on a weighted average valuation basis.

Task 1.1

Complete the stock card on the next page for chemical XR for the month of July, using the weighted average method.

(Due to the breakdown of a processing machine during the last week of July, there were no further issues of XR in July after those shown.)

STOCK CARD

Stock item: Chemical XR (direct material)   **Unit:** litre

Date	Receipts			Issues			Stock		
	Quantity	Unit price £	Total cost £	Quantity	Unit price £	Total £	Quantity	Unit price £	Total £
1 July							12,000	3	36,000
7 July				7,000					
10 July	10,000	3.06	30,600						
14 July				7,000					
17 July	10,000	3.06	30,600						
21 July				8,000					
31 July (balance)									

ADDITIONAL DATA

The following data relates to the direct labour employees who work on production of Chem-Base for the month of July:

Normal time hours worked	5,520 hours
Overtime hours worked	400 hours
Total hours of production	5,920 hours
Idle time due to machine breakdown	780 hours
Total labour hours paid for	6,700 hours

The normal time rate for the idle time is to be treated as an indirect cost.

Normal time rate per hour = £7.00

Overtime premium = £3.50. Total overtime premium is treated as an indirect cost.

Task 1.2

Complete the table below for the direct labour employees for the month of July.

	Total cost £	Direct cost £	Indirect cost £
Normal time hours worked			
Overtime hours worked			
Total hours of production			
Idle time (machine breakdown)			
Total labour hours paid for			

ADDITIONAL DATA

The Processing Division of Chem-Pro Ltd has four departments, shown below with available information:

	Net book value of fixed assets	% time of IT services	% requisitions
Production	£200,000	40%	90%
Stores	£40,000	20%	-
IT Services	£8,000	-	-
Administration	£12,000	40%	10%
	£260,000	100%	100%

The monthly budgeted overheads for the Division amount to £46,500, as shown in the table on the next page. Some budgeted overheads have already been allocated and Premises Costs have been apportioned to the four departments.

Task 1.3

Complete the table on the next page using suitable bases for:

*   apportionment of Depreciation

*   re-apportionment of IT Services overheads

*   re-apportionment of Stores overheads

Note: do not re-apportion Administration overheads.

Chem-Pro Ltd: Processing Division Monthly Overhead Budget

	Basis	Total £	Production £	Stores £	IT Services £	Administration £
Allocated overheads	Allocated	29,300	8,860	4,000	9,240	7,200
Premises costs	Floor area	12,000	9,000	1,800	600	600
Depreciation		5,200				
Subtotals						
Reapportion IT Services						
Subtotals						
Re-apportion Stores						
Totals						

ADDITIONAL DATA

The total monthly Budgeted Production Overhead from your answer to Task 1.3 is to be used to calculate the Production Overhead absorption rate, based on budgeted machine hours. The monthly budgeted machine hours are 11,200 hours.

Task 1.4

Calculate the Production Overhead absorption rate.

ADDITIONAL DATA

The actual production overheads in July amounted to £39,000. Due to the machine breakdown, the actual machine hours for the month of July were only 8,510 hours.

Task 1.5

(a)   Using your answer to Task 1.4, calculate the Production Overheads absorbed on the actual 8,510 machine hours and calculate the over or under absorption for the month of July.

(b)   Comment briefly on the reasons why the over or under absorption of Production overhead calculated in (a) above has occurred.

ADDITIONAL DATA

The Processing Division uses process costing in order to determine the cost per litre of the output of Chem-Base. The direct material XR is input to the process. The normal loss is 10% of the material input and this has no scrap value.

Task 1.6

Refer to your answers as follows:

Task 1.1	to determine the total amount in litres and the cost of direct material XR issued to the process during July
Task 1.2	to identify the total direct labour cost for July
Task 1.5	to identify the production overhead absorbed during July

Use these figures and the additional data given above to complete the Process Account for the month of July.

From the completed Process Account, calculate the cost per litre of output of Chem-Base.

Process Account: Chem-Pro Processing for July

Dr					Cr
	Litres	£		Litres	£
Material XR					
Direct labour					
Production overheads absorbed					

Cost per litre of output of Chem-Base =

SECTION 2

You should spend about 90 minutes on this section.

ADDITIONAL DATA

The output of Chem-Base from the Processing Division of Chem-Pro Ltd is sold to the Resins Division of the same company at a price of £8.00 per litre. The Resins Division manufactures three products, P, Q and R. You are given information relating to these products in the table below.

Task 2.1

Complete the three rows that are left blank in the table below.

Product	P	Q	R
Demand per month (units to be made and sold)	3,000	3,000	4,500
Chem-Base per unit (litres)	2.5	2	3
Costs per unit:	£	£	£
Direct material cost (Chem-Base)			
Other variable costs	30	30	30
Total variable costs			
Selling price per unit	100	96	105
Contribution per unit			

Task 2.2

Assuming sufficient resources are available to produce the full demand for each of the products P, Q and R, calculate the total contribution obtained per month in the Resins Division by completing the table below. Refer to your answer to Task 2.1 where required.

Chem-Pro Resins Division Monthly Contribution	Demand (units)	Contribution per unit (£)	Total contribution (£)
Product P	3,000		
Product Q	3,000		
Product R	4,500		
Total contribution per month			

ADDITIONAL DATA

The processing machine breakdown in July will result in a shortage of Chem-Base for the Resins Division to use in August. The total Chem-Base available for production of resins P, Q and R will be 19,800 litres for the month.

Task 2.3

Complete the table below to determine the ranking of the three products P, Q and R in terms of their contribution per litre of the material Chem-Base. Refer to your answer to Task 2.1 where required.

Product	P	Q	R
Demand (units)	3,000	3,000	4,500
Chem-Base per unit (litres)	2.5	2	3
Contribution per unit	£	£	£
Contribution per unit per litre of Chem-Base			
Ranking			

Task 2.4

(a)   Complete the table below to determine the production quantities of P, Q, and R that will maximise the Resins Division profit in August, when only 19,800 litres of Chem-Base are available:

Ranking	Product	Units of production and sales	Chem-Base per unit (litres)	Total used (litres)
1				
2				
3				

(b)   Calculate for the Resins Division for August:

- the units of production and sales lost due to the shortage of Chem-Base
- the total contribution lost due to the shortage of Chem-Base

ADDITIONAL DATA

The managers of Chem-Pro Ltd are concerned that machine breakdowns result in financial losses to the company. They are considering upgrading machinery to make it more reliable.

An initial investment (Year 0) of £120,000 would be required. Forecasts of the resulting cash flow (savings) over the following four years are:

	Cash savings
Year 1	£50,000
Year 2	£55,000
Year 3	£60,000
Year 4	£60,000

The residual value of the project at the end of the four years (Year 4) is expected to be £30,000.

A discount rate of 10% is to be used in appraisal of the investment.

Task 2.5

Using the table below for your workings, calculate the payback period and the net present value for the proposed investment in the upgrade of machinery.

Chem-Pro Ltd Proposal to upgrade machinery				
	Cash flow £	**Accumulated cash flow** £	**10% Present value factor**	**Discounted cash flow** £
Year 0			1.000	
Year 1			0.909	
Year 2			0.826	
Year 3			0.751	
Year 4			0.683	
Net Present Value				

Payback period:

Task 2.6

Referring to your answers to Task 2.5, write a short report on the proposed upgrade to the managers of Chem-Pro Ltd. Your report should include:

*   a recommendation as to whether to proceed with the project
*   one advantage of the upgrade that is not shown in the figures in your analysis

Please see the report format on the next page.

REPORT

To:

From:

Date:

Subject:

Unit 6
Recording and evaluating costs and revenues

Practice examination 3: Gift Limited
(based on AAT sample material) © AAT, 2003

NVQ Element coverage

6.1 record and analyse information relating to direct costs and revenues

6.2 record and analyse information relating to the allocation, apportionment and absorption of overhead costs

6.3 prepare and evaluate estimates of costs and revenues

Suggested time allocation

Three hours and fifteen minutes (to include a recommended fifteen minutes reading time).

PRACTICE EXAMINATION 3
GIFT LIMITED

This examination is in TWO sections.

You have to show competence in BOTH sections.

You should therefore attempt and aim to complete EVERY task in BOTH sections.

Blank space for workings is available on these pages, but all essential workings should be included within your answers, where appropriate.

You should spend about 90 minutes on each section.

Both sections are based on Gift Ltd.

DATA

Gift Ltd manufactures and sells toys. You work as an accounting technician at Gift Ltd, reporting to the Finance Director.

All toys are manufactured using plastic. The biggest selling item is Meg, a toy doll made from pink plastic. The company operates an integrated absorption costing system. Stocks are valued on a first in first out basis.

The Finance Director has given you the tasks that follow in Sections 1 and 2.

SECTION 1

You should spend about 90 minutes on this section.

Task 1.1

Complete the stock card (on the next page) for pink plastic using the FIFO method for valuing issues to production and stocks of materials.

Use the boxes shown below the stock card to show your answers.

STOCK CARD

Product: Pink plastic

Date	Receipts Quantity kgs	Cost per kg £	Total cost £	Issues Quantity kgs	Cost per kg £	Total cost £	Balance Quantity kgs	Total cost £
b/f 1.11.03							10,000	10,000
6.11.03	20,000	1.10	22,000				30,000	32,000
11.11.03				16,000				
17.11.03	10,000	1.20	12,000					
19.11.03				20,000				

**issue
11.11.03**

**issue
19.11.03**

ADDITIONAL DATA

All issues of pink plastic are for the manufacture of Meg dolls. The following cost accounting codes are used to record material costs:

Code number	Description
1000	Stock of pink plastic
1100	Work in progress – Meg dolls
3000	Creditors control

Task 1.2

Complete the table below to record separately the two purchases and two issues of pink plastic in the cost accounting records.

Date	Code	Dr	Cr
6 Nov	1000		
6 Nov	3000		
11 Nov	1000		
11 Nov	1100		
17 Nov	1000		
17 Nov	3000		
19 Nov	1000		
19 Nov	1100		

ADDITIONAL DATA

Direct labour overtime payments are included in direct costs. The following data relates to the production of Meg dolls for November:

Total direct labour hours worked	12,000 hours
Normal time hours	10,600 hours
Overtime hours	1,400 hours
Normal time rate per hour	£6 per hour
Overtime premium per hour	£3 per hour

Task 1.3

Calculate the total cost of direct labour for November.

ADDITIONAL DATA

Gift Ltd has the following departments: Warehouse, Manufacturing, Sales, Accounting.

The budgeted and actual fixed overheads of the company for November were as follows:

	£
Depreciation	7,400
Rent	2,500
Other property overheads	3,200
Accounting overheads	6,250
Staff costs:	
Warehouse	4,230
Indirect manufacturing	3,015
Sales	6,520
Accounting	5,160
Total budgeted and actual fixed overheads	38,275

The following information is also relevant:

Department	% of floor space occupied	Net book value of fixed assets £000
Warehouse	15%	180
Manufacturing	70%	540
Sales	10%	-
Accounting	5%	80
	100%	800

Overheads are allocated and apportioned between departments using the most appropriate basis.

Task 1.4

Complete the following table showing the allocation and apportionment of fixed overheads between the four departments.

Fixed overheads for November	Basis	Total £	Warehouse £	Manufacturing £	Sales £	Accounting £
Depreciation		7,400				
Rent		2,500				
Other property overheads		3,200				
Accounting overheads		6,250				
Staff costs		18,925				
		38,275				

ADDITIONAL DATA

Manufacturing fixed overheads are absorbed on the basis of budgeted direct labour hours. The following information relates to the manufacturing department for November:

- The budgeted number of direct labour hours was 20,000 hours.

- The actual direct labour hours worked producing Meg dolls were 12,000 hours.

- 36,000 Meg dolls were produced with a material cost for pink plastic of £39,200.

Task 1.5

Use the data from Task 1.4 to calculate the budgeted fixed overhead absorption rate for the manufacturing department for November.

Task 1.6

Use the information from Tasks 1.3 and 1.5 to complete the table below to show:

       (a)   the total cost of production

       (b)   the unit cost of production of a Meg doll for November

Product: Meg doll	£
Direct costs	
Pink plastic	
Direct labour	
Indirect costs	
Manufacturing department overheads	
Total cost of production	
Number of Meg dolls produced	
Unit cost of production (to the nearest penny)	

SECTION 2

You should spend about 90 minutes on this section.

DATA

In addition to producing Meg dolls, the company manufactures and sells three types of doll house, products E, C and R. The expected monthly costs and sales information for each product is as follows:

Product	E	C	R
Sales and production units	2,000	1,500	500
Machine hours per month	200	225	175
Total sales revenue	£60,000	£60,000	£30,000
Total direct materials	£20,000	£16,500	£6,000
Total direct labour	£32,000	£24,000	£10,000
Total variable overheads	£4,000	£2,625	£3,500

The total expected monthly fixed costs relating to the production of all doll houses are £4,800.

Task 2.1

Complete the table below to show for each product the expected contribution per unit.

Product	E £	C £	R £
Selling price per unit			
Less: Unit variable costs			
Direct materials			
Direct labour			
Variable overheads			
Contribution per unit			

Task 2.2

If the company only manufactures product E, calculate the number of units it would need to make and sell each month to cover the fixed costs of £4,800.

ADDITIONAL DATA

The breakdown of a machine used in the manufacture of doll houses has reduced available machine time from 600 to 365 hours. The Finance Director asks you to calculate the contribution of each doll house per machine hour.

Task 2.3

Use the data from Task 2.1 to complete the table below.

Product	E £	C £	R £
Contribution per unit			
Machine hours per unit			
Contribution per machine hour			

Task 2.4

Use the data from Task 2.3 to calculate how many units of products E, C and R the company should make and sell to maximize its profits using 365 machine hours.

ADDITIONAL DATA

The company requires an annual rate of return of 10% on any new project. The Managing Director has asked you to appraise the financial effects of introducing a new doll house. You are given the following information relating to this product:

	Year 1 £000	Year 2 £000	Year 3 £000	Year 4 £000	Year 5 £000
Design costs	80				
Sales revenues		30	50	160	50
Variable costs		15	25	80	25
10% Present value factor	0.909	0.826	0.751	0.683	0.621

Task 2.5

Calculate for the new doll house project:

(a)   the payback period

(b)   the net present value

Task 2.6

Use the data from Task 2.5 to prepare a report to the Managing Director on the new doll house project. Your report should:

(a)   identify TWO additional items of information relevant to appraising this project

(b)   recommend whether to accept or reject the project based on its net present value

---

REPORT

To:

From:

Date:

APPENDIX - SAMPLE FORMATS

the structure of a total cost statement and a profit statement

	TOTAL COST STATEMENT	
		£
	Direct materials	x
add	Direct labour	x
add	Direct expenses	x
equals	PRIME COST	x
add	Production overheads	x
equals	PRODUCTION COST	x
add	Selling and distribution costs ⌐	x
add	Administration costs ── ├ non-production overheads	x
add	Finance costs ── ┘	x
equals	TOTAL COST	x

	PROFIT STATEMENT	
		£
	Sales	x
less	Total cost	x
equals	PROFIT	x

the structure of a manufacturing account and a profit and loss account

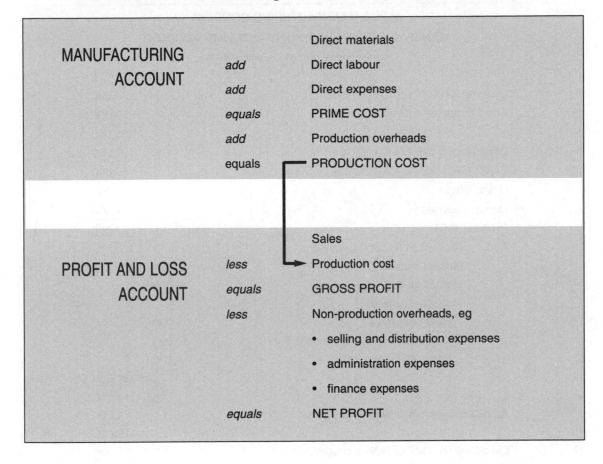

MANUFACTURING
ACCOUNT

	Direct materials
add	Direct labour
add	Direct expenses
equals	PRIME COST
add	Production overheads
equals	PRODUCTION COST

PROFIT AND LOSS
ACCOUNT

	Sales
less	Production cost
equals	GROSS PROFIT
less	Non-production overheads, eg
	• selling and distribution expenses
	• administration expenses
	• finance expenses
equals	NET PROFIT

an example of a manufacturing and profit and loss account

ALPHA MANUFACTURING COMPANY
MANUFACTURING AND PROFIT AND LOSS ACCOUNT
for the year ended 31 December 2004

	£	£
Opening stock of direct materials		5,000
Add Purchases of direct materials		50,000
		55,000
Less Closing stock of direct materials		6,000
COST OF DIRECT MATERIALS USED		49,000
Direct labour		26,000
Direct expenses		2,500
PRIME COST		77,500
Add Production (factory) overheads:		
Indirect materials	2,000	
Indirect labour	16,000	
Indirect expenses:		
Rent of factory	5,000	
Depreciation of factory machinery	10,000	
Factory light and heat	4,000	
		37,000
		114,500
Add Opening stock of work-in-progress		4,000
		118,500
Less Closing stock of work-in-progress		3,000
PRODUCTION COST OF GOODS COMPLETED		115,500
Sales		195,500
Opening stock of finished goods	6,500	
Production cost of goods completed	115,500	
	122,000	
Less Closing stock of finished goods	7,500	
COST OF SALES		114,500
Gross profit		81,000
Less Non-production overheads:		
Selling and distribution expenses	38,500	
Administration expenses	32,000	
Finance expenses	3,500	
		74,000
Net profit		7,000